Practical Liquid Chromatography

An Introduction

R. W. YOST
L. S. ETTRE
R. D. CONLON

PERKIN-ELMER

1980

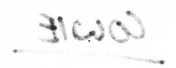

The Perkin-Elmer Corp., Chromatography Division, Main Ave.,
(MS-150), Norwalk, CT 06856, U.S.A. Tel: (203) 762-1000

Bodenseewerk Perkin-Elmer & Co., GmbH, Postfach 1120,
7770 Ueberlingen, Federal Republic of Germany   Tel: (07551) 811

Perkin-Elmer Ltd,, Post Office Lane, Beaconsfield,
Bucks HP9 1QA, England   Tel: Beaconsfield 6161

Library of Congress Cataloging in Publication Data

Main entry under title:

Practical Liquid Chromatography - An Introduction

1. Chemistry, Analytic   2. Liquid Chromatography

I.   R. W. Yost 1931 -
     L. S. Ettre 1922 -
     R. D. Conlon 1930 -

II. Title

     544.924
     545.89

First printing: September 1980.

PRINTED IN THE UNITED STATES OF AMERICA

TABLE OF CONTENTS

The purpose of this book is to provide a source to the practical liquid chromatographer where the most important relationships can be found. It does not replace a general LC textbook, and it does not intend to explain liquid chromatography theory in depth; rather, it should simply be used as a reference when doing day-to-day analysis.

I would like to thank the people who were responsible for making this book possible: Roy Yost who started the project and had the tenacity to see its completion; Leslie Ettre for his excellent organization and ability to complete the project in a short time; Ralph Conlon for his technical guidance; and last but not least, Margaret Primost for her desire to spend long hours at the typewriter.

Without the efforts of these people, this book would never have become a reality.

Norwalk, Connecticut, U.S.A.
April 21, 1980

R.L. Hannah
Senior Product Manager
Chromatography

Practical Liquid Chromatography

An Introduction

Part One:
Introduction and Overview

1.1 GENERAL CONSIDERATIONS

Liquid chromatography is one of the versions of
chromatography, the most widely used analytical
technique. Chromatographic processes, in general,
can be defined as follows:

Chromatography is essentially a physical method
of separation in which the components to be
separated are distributed between two phases;
one of them a stationary bed, while the other
moves percolating through this bed. The chromatographic process occurs as a result of repeated
sorption-desorption acts during the movement of
the sample components along the stationary bed,
and the separation is due to differences in the
distribution coefficients of the individual
sample components.

"Stationary bed" is used as a general term to
denote any of the different forms in which the
stationary phase may be used: it may be packed in
a column, spread as a layer, etc. The mobile
phase may be gaseous or liquid.

In gas chromatography, the mobile phase is a gas
while in liquid chromatography, our present
subject, it is a liquid. Liquid chromatography can
be carried out in various systems depending on the
physical form of the stationary phase. In thin-
layer and paper chromatography, it is spread as a
layer (plane chromatography), while in column
chromatography, it is packed in a "column", a
relatively narrow tube. The subject of this book

3

is "Liquid Column Chromatography" although, naturally, some of the aspects can be applied as well to plane chromatography.

There are many ways to further divide liquid column chromatography. If this division is based on the nature of the stationary phase and the separation process, four modes can be specified.

- In adsorption chromatography - the stationary phase is an adsorbent and the separation is based on repeated adsorption-desorption steps.

- In partition chromatography - the separation is not based on adsorption, but rather partition between the mobile and stationary phases.

- In ion-exchange chromatography - the stationary bed has an ionically charged surface of opposite charge to the sample. This technique is used almost exclusively with ionic or ioni- zable samples. The stronger the charge on the sample, the stronger will it be attracted to the ionic surface and thus, the longer it will take to elute. The mobile phase is an aqueous buffer, where pH and polarity are used to control elution time from the column.

- In size exclusion chromatography - the column is filled with material having precisely controlled pore sizes, and the sample is simply screened or filtered according to molecular size differences as it is washed through the column. Mainly for historical reasons, this technique is also called gel filtration or gel chromatography although, today, the stationary phase is not restricted to a "gel".

Concerning the first two modes, it is sometimes not equivocal whether the dominant process is adsorption or partition or both. For this reason, in practice, two or more modes are defined depending on the relative polarity of the two phases: normal and reversed-phase chromatography.

In normal phase chromatography, the stationary bed is strongly polar in nature (e.g., silica), and the mobile phase nonpolar (such as n-hexane or tetrahydrofuran). Polar samples are thus retained on the column longer than less (or non) polar materials.

Reversed-phase chromatography is the exact inverse of this. The stationary bed is nonpolar (hydrocarbon) in nature, while the mobile phase is a polar liquid, such as water or an alcohol. Here the more nonpolar the material is, the longer it will be retained.

Sometimes the mobile phase may be modified to adjust its polarity. In the normal mode, this may be done by the addition of a more polar substance, while in reversed-phase chromatography, the additive is a less polar substance.

Figure 1-1 visualizes these two techniques indicating the order of elution of sample components of different polarity.

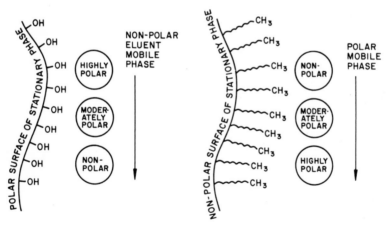

Fig. 1-1. *Graphical illustration of normal and reversed-phase liquid chromatography. The circles represent the types of compounds present in the sample; their relative position to the direction of the mobile phase flow indicates their order of elution.*

1.2 NOMENCLATURE

As we shall see below, liquid column chromatography is the oldest chromatographic method, and scientists of various countries contributed to its evolution. It is inevitable, in such a case, that various terms and names are used by different scientists.

Recently, various national and international bodies started to standardize the chromatographic nomenclature and in this book, we are following, whenever possible, their recommendations. We particularly refer here to two documents which we are following - the first, published by the Chromatography Nomenclature Committee of the Analytical Division of the International Union of Pure and Applied Chemistry (I.U.P.A.C.), and the other by the Committee E-19 on Chromatography of the American Society for Testing and Materials (ASTM). The first published recommendation for a standardized chromatography nomenclature which may be adapted to any of the modes, while the second developed separate nomenclatures for gas and liquid chromatography which, however, are naturally interrelated. The pertinent documents are:

Recommendations on Nomenclature for Chromatography.
Pure and Applied Chemistry 37, 447-462 (1974)

Liquid Chromatography Terms and Relationships.
ASTM E 682-79; Vol. 42 of 1979 ASTM Books of Standards.

1.3 HISTORY OF LIQUID CHROMATOGRAPHY

Although certain investigations in the second part of the last century may be termed as the precursors of "chromatography", it is clearly established that the technique was first developed by M.S. Tswett, a Russian botanist, for the separation and isolation of plant pigments. The first description of the method was included in a paper presented in 1903 and then, a detailed report on the method and its application was published by him in 1906. Tswett also coined the name from Greek words meaning "color writing", referring to the bands of different colored substances which he separated on the powdered chalk columns he used, immediately emphasizing, however, that the technique is not restricted to the separation of colored substances.

A relatively long period of time went after Tswett with no further development of the technique; in this "dormant period" only the work of Palmer, an American scientist, is noteworthy. Then in 1930/31, the method was revitalized in the laboratories at Heidelberg, Germany, by Kuhn and E. Lederer. Within a few years, liquid column chromatography became a universally used technique without which the significant achievements in the chemistry of complex natural organic substances and in bio-chemistry would have been impossible.

In the 20 years following the rediscovery of chromatography, the technique was further expanded and the individual variants developed. A particularly important milestone was the development of gas-liquid partition chromatography by Martin and James in 1952. This technique found immediate important applications and the widespread interest in the technique initiated basic research on the theory of chromatography and in the development of standardized instrumentation in gas chromatography. This, in turn, cross-fertilized also liquid chromatography by generalizing the theory and applying it specifically to this variant. This occurred in the 1960's resulting in a new explosion-the development of modern liquid column chromatography now called high performance liquid chromatography (H.P.L.C.), a development still continuing today.

The milestones of the evolution of chromatography are listed in Table 1-1. For those who are particularly interested in these, three publications are recommended:

L. S. Ettre and C. Horvath, The Foundation of Modern Liquid Chromatography.
Analytical Chemistry, 47 (4), 422A-444A (April 1975)

L. S. Ettre and A. Zlatkis (editors), 75 years of Chromatography - A Historical Dialogue. Elsevier, Amsterdam, 1979

L. S. Ettre, Evolution of Liquid Chromatography - A Historical Overview. In High Performance Liquid Chromatography - Advances and Perspectives, Vol.1 edited by C. Horvath, Academic Press, New York,1980.

TABLE 1-1

MILESTONES IN LIQUID CHROMATOGRAPHY

1903 On March 21, M.S. Tswett presents a paper at Warsaw in which the principles of the chromatographic method are first outlined. (1)

1906 Tswett's two basic papers are published in the Berichte der deutschen Botanischen Gesellschaft. (2-3)

1914 Five papers by L.S. Palmer and C. Eckles published in the Journal of Biological Chemistry in which chromatography is extensively utilized. (4-7)

1931 The three papers by E. Lederer and R. Kuhn on the utilization of chromatography for the separation of carotenoids. (8-10)

1936 The book on chromatography by L. Zechmeister and L. Cholnoky. (11)

1938 N.A. Izmailov and M.S. Shraiber first described "thin-layer chromatography". (12)

1938 T.I. Taylor and H.C. Urey utilized ion-exchange chromatography with zeolites. (13)

1939 O. Samuelson first used synthetic ion-exchange resins in chromatographic separation. (14-15)

1940- Tiselius and his group develop frontal analysis
1943 and displacement development. (16-19)

1941 First paper on (liquid-liquid) partition chromatography by A.J.P. Martin and R.L.M. Synge. (20)

1944 First paper on paper chromatography by R. Consden, A.H. Gordon and A.J.P. Martin. (21)

1948 Nobel Prize in Chemistry to A.Tiselius "for his work on electrophoresis and adsorption analysis."

1950 Reversed-phase liquid chromatography described by G.A. Howard and A.J.P. Martin. (22)

1951 S. Moore and W.H. Stein described the separation of amino acids on synthetic ion-exchange resins. (23)

1952 Gradient elution technique described by R. S. Alm, R.J.P. Williams and A. Tiselius. (24)

1952 Nobel Prize in Chemistry to A.J.P. Martin and R.L.M. Synge "for the invention of partition chromatography."

1956 Development of the theory of chromatographic separation by J.J. van Deemter, F.J. Zuiderweg and A. Klinkenberg. (25)

1959 First paper on gel (permeation) chromatography by J. Porath and P. Flodin using dextran gels. (26)

1961 First papers of L.R. Snyder on linear elution adsorption chromatography. (27-29)

1962 J.C. Moore introduces macroporous polymer gels for gel permeation chromatography. (30,31)

1965- Development of modern high performance liquid
1969 chromatography by I. Halasz (32-34); C. Horvath (35-37); J.F.K. Huber (38-41); J.H. Knox (42-43); J.J. Kirkland (44-47); V. Pretorius (48); R.P.W. Scott (49-50); L.R. Snyder (51-53) and others (see 54-55).

References to Table 1-1

1. M.S. Tswett, Tr. Protok, Varshav, Obschch. Estestvoispyt. Otd. Biol. 14 (1903; publ. 1905). English translation: G. Hesse and H. Weil: Michael Tswett's First Paper on Chromatography. M. Woelm, Eschwege, 1954.

2. M.S. Tswett, Ber. deut. botan. Ges. 24, 316-323 (1906).

3. M.S. Tswett, Ber. deut. botan. Ges. 24, 384-393 (1906)

4. L.S. Palmer and C. Eckles, J. Biol. Chem 17, 191-210 (1914).

5. L.S. Palmer and C. Eckles, J. Biol. Chem. 17, 211-221 (1914).

6. L.S. Palmer and C. Eckles, J. Biol Chem. 17, 223-236 (1914).

7. L. S. Palmer and C. Eckles, J. Biol. Chem. 17, 245-249 (1914).

8. R. Kuhn and E. Lederer, Naturwissenschaften 19, 306 (1931)

9. R. Kuhn, A. Winterstein and E. Lederer, Z. physiol. Chem. 197, 141-160 (1931).

10. R. Kuhn and E. Lederer, Ber. 64, 1349-1357 (1931).

11. L. Zechmeister and L. Cholnoky, Die Chromatographische Adsorptionsmethode, Springer, Wien, 1936; 2nd ed. 1938. English translation of the second edition: Principles and Practice of Chromatography, Chapman and Hall, London, and Wiley, New York, 1941.

12. N.A. Izmailov and M.S. Shraiber, Farmatsiya 3, 1 (1938). English translation: N. Pelick, H. R. Bollinger and H.K. Mangold in Advances in Chromatography Vol. 3, J.C. Giddings and R.A. Keller, eds. M. Dekker, Inc. New York, 1966; pp. 85-118.

13. T.I. Taylor and H. C. Urey, J. Chem. Phys. 6, 429-438 (1938).

14. O. Samuelson, Z. Anal. Chem. 116, 328 (1939).

15. O. Samuelson, Svensk. Kem. Tidskr. 51, 195-206 (1939).

16. A. Tiselius, Arkiv. Kem. Mineral. Geol. 14B (22), 1-5 (1940).

17. A. Tiselius, Arkiv. Kem. Mineral. Geol. 14B, (32) 1-8 (1941)

18. A. Tiselius and S. Claesson, Arkiv. Kem. Mineral. Geol. 15B (18), 1-6 (1942).

19. A. Tiselius, Arkiv. Kem. Mineral. Geol. 16A (18), 1-11 (1943).

20. A.J.P. Martin and R.L.M. Synge, Biochem. J. 35, 1358-1368 (1941).

21. R. Consden, A. H. Gordon and A.J.P. Martin, Biochem. J. 38, 224-232 (1944).

22. G.A. Howard and A.J.P. Martin, Biochem. J. 46, 532-538 (1950).

23. S. Moore and W.H. Stein, J. Biol. Chem. 192, 663-681 (1951).

24. R.S. Alm, R.J.P. Williams and A. Tiselius, Acta Chem. Scan. 6, 826-836 (1952).

25. J.J. van Deemter, F.J. Zuiderweg and A. Klinkenberg, Chem. Eng. Sci. 5, 271-289 (1956).

26. J. Porath and P. Flodin, Nature (London) 183, 1657-1659 (1959).

27. L.R. Snyder, J. Chromatogr. 5, 430-441 (1961).

28. L.R. Snyder, J. Chromatogr. 6, 22-52 (1961).

29. L.R. Snyder, Anal. Chem. 33, 1527-1534, 1535-1538, 1538-1543 (1961).

30. Anon. Chem. Eng. News 40 (51), 43-44 (1962).

31. J.C. Moore, J. Polymer Sci. A2, 835-843 (1964).

32. I. Halasz, H.O. Gerlach, A. Kroneisen and P. Walking, Z. Anal. Chem. 234, 81-97 (1968).

33. I. Halasz, H.O. Gerlach, A. Kroneisen and P. Walking, Z. Anal. Chem. 234, 97-108 (1968).

34. I. Halasz and P. Walking, J. Chromatogr. Sci. 7, 129-136 (1969).

35. C.G. Horvath and S.R. Lipsky, Nature, (London) 211, 748-749 (1966).

36. C.G. Horvath, B.A. Preiss and S.R. Lipsky, Anal. Chem. 39, 1422-1428 (1967).

37. C. Horvath and S.R. Lipsky, J. Chromatogr. Sci. 7, 109-116 (1969).

38. J.F.K. Huber, Symp. on Recent Developments in Chromatography, College of Technology, Liverpool, May 13-14, 1966.

39. J.F.K. Huber and J.A.R.J. Hulsman, Anal. Chem. Acta 38, 305-313 (1967).

40. J.F.K. Huber, J. Chromatogr. Sci. 7, 85-90 (1969).

41. J.F.K. Huber, J. Chromatogr. Sci. 7, 172-176 (1969).

42. J.H. Knox, Anal. Chem. 38, 253-261 (1966).

43. D.S. Horne, J.H. Knox and L. McLaren, Sep. Sci. 1, 531-555 (1966).

44. J.J. Kirkland, Anal. Chem. 40, 391-396 (1968).

45. J.J. Kirland, J. Chromatogr. Sci. 7, 7-12 (1969).

46. J.J. Kirkland, Anal. Chem. 41, 218-220 (1969).

47. J.J. Kirkland, J. Chromatogr. Sci. 7, 361-365 (1969).

48. T.W. Smuts, F.A. Niekerk and V. Pretorius, J. Gas Chromatogr. 5, 190-196 (1967).

49. R.P.W. Scott, D.W.J. Blackburn and T. Wilkins, J. Gas Chromatogr. 5, 183-189 (1967).

50. R.P.W. Scott and J.G. Lawrence, J. Chromatogr. Sci. 7, 65-71 (1969).

51. L.R. Snyder, Principles of Adsorption Chromatography, M. Dekker, Inc. New York. 1968.

52. L.R. Snyder, Anal. Chem. 39, 698-704, 705-709 (1967).

53. L.R. Snyder and D.L. Saunders, J. Chromatogr. Sci. 7, 195-208 (1969).

54. J.V. Mortimer, reporter, Liquid Chromatography Discussion Section. In Gas Chromatography 1966, (Rome Symposium) A.B. Littlewood, ed., Institute of Petroleum, London, 1967; pp. 414-418.

55. L.S. Ettre and A. Zlatkis, eds., <u>75 Years of Chromatography - A Historical Dialogue</u>.Elsevier, Amsterdam. 1979.

1.4 MODERN LIQUID CHROMATOGRAPHY

As we have seen earlier, liquid column chromatography is the oldest chromatographic technique; it has been in use since 1903. What is, then, the difference between modern liquid column chromatography, HPLC, and the classical techniques?

In classical column chromatography, the columns were open tubes, typically 15-20 cm x 1-4 cm ID. The packing was a coarse material and the columns were individually prepared each time. The mobile phase* flow was achieved by gravity feeding of the column. In earlier work, the process was stopped before the first sample component would emerge from the column and the separated components were revealed in the form of colored rings. Thus the column with these "rings" was called the <u>chromatogram</u>. If the individual components were to be obtained in pure form, the column packing was slowly removed in fractions from the tube and the pure components extracted. In the second part of the 1930's, a new method started to gain acceptance slowly replacing the old technique. Now the mobile phase flow was not stopped and the individual components were washed out of the column and collected in fractions. Obviously, both are slow and time consuming methods and a separation may have taken hours followed then by the examination of the individual fractions. We should add, that the application of the sample to the top of the column at the beginning of the analysis also

---

* In classical liquid column chromatography, the term "solvent" was used to express the mobile phase and even today, we can sometimes find this usage. It is highly misleading because in partition chromatography, the (liquid) stationary phase has also been called the "solvent". For this reason, modern nomenclature recommendations advise not to use it and specify the term <u>mobile</u> <u>phase</u>, instead.

required considerable skill. Figure 1-2 illustrates classical liquid chromatography sometimes
called <u>gravity</u> <u>flow</u> <u>chromatography</u> in order to
differentiate it from the modern techniques.

*Fig. 1-2. Schematic representation of classical
(gravity flow) liquid chromatography.*

We should not underestimate the power of classical
liquid chromatography and the results obtained
with its use. Exceptional separations have been
performed and the revolutionary evolution in the
chemistry of complex natural substances which
we had witnessed in the 1930's and 40's, could
not have been achieved without chromatography.
Still, its drawbacks - mainly slowness and the
need for skill and manual operation - represented
serious problems particularly for use as a routine
analytical tool.

Gas-liquid partition chromatography emerging in
1952 - and following from the basic work on liquid-
liquid partition chromatography by Martin and
Synge - had the main advantage of speed and auto-

mation. Its explosive development in the following decade overshadowed liquid chromatography particularly since a number of samples previously investigated by LC could also be analyzed by this technique. However, it also became apparent that, due to either insufficient volatility or thermal instability, many samples simply could not be handled by GC. Thus, by the beginning of the 60's a number of researchers began to look into the possibilities of how to improve the technique of liquid chromatography. In their work, they were aided by the significant achievements in the theory of the chromatographic process which showed the ways how to overcome the slowness of diffusion in liquid phase as compared to gas phases. The conclusion was to use much smaller particles; this however, needed higher inlet pressures and new detectors capable of handling low flow rates and detecting small amounts of substances. The solution of these problems made the evolution of modern liquid chromatography possible.

Modern liquid chromatography - as compared with the classical technique - is characterized by:

- small diameter (2-5 mm), reusable columns;

- column packings with very small (3-50 μm) particles and the development of new substances to be used as stationary phases;

- relatively high inlet pressures and controlled flow of the mobile phase;

- precise sample introduction without the need for larger samples;

- special continuous detectors capable of handling small flow rates and detecting very small amounts;

- automated standardized instruments;

- rapid analysis; and

- high resolution.

The controlled flow of the mobile phase is

achieved with help of high pressure pumps. Controlled flow results in more reproducible operation which in turn provides better accuracy and precision. The new detectors yield a final chromatogram and can feed information to data systems.

Among these characteristics, pressure was selected at the beginning as the principal criterion of modern liquid chromatography which hence was named as high pressure liquid chromatography or HPLC. This was, however, an unfortunate term because it seems to indicate that the improved performance is primarily due to the high pressure. This is, however, not true. Naturally, some pressure is needed to permit a given flow rate of the mobile phase; otherwise, pressure is a negative factor not contributing to the improvement in separation. Recognizing this, most experienced chromato-graphers today, refer to the technique as high performance liquid chromatography - still permitting the use of the acronym HPLC. In fact, more and more chemists are returning to the term "liquid chromatography" when speaking about the technique.

As compared to gas chromatography, modern liquid chromatography has one important difference. We have seen earlier that in chromatography, separation is based on specific interactions between the sample molecules and the stationary and mobile phase. In gas chromatography, the mobile phase does not participate in these inter-actions. Being essentially an inert gas, the only role of the mobile phase is to carry the sample molecules through the system. Thus, in gas chroma-tography, separation is based on the interactions between the sample and the stationary phase. The situation is, however, different in liquid chroma-tography - here the mobile phase is not "inert" anymore as far as these interactions are concerned but has an active role in them. Thus, in liquid chromatography, we have an additional variable which can be properly selected to improve the separation power of the system.

1.5 THE LIQUID CHROMATOGRAPHY SYSTEM

Figure 1-3 presents the functional schematic of a
general liquid chromatography system. As seen,
the basic components of such a system are a <u>pump</u>
to propel the mobile phase; a device for <u>sample</u>
<u>introduction</u>; a <u>column</u> containing the stationary
phase; and a <u>detector</u> to determine what separation
has taken place and provide data permitting the
qualitative and quantitative evaluation of the
results. This can be accomplished by simply
<u>recording</u> the response of the detector in the form
of a <u>chromatogram</u> (a response vs time curve)
and/or with the help of <u>data handling</u> equipment.
The individual sample components separated in the
column can also be <u>collected</u>.

In this introductory part, we should familiarize
ourselves with the various parts of the LC system;
more detailed information will be found in the
subsequent parts. We shall start with the two
phases influencing the separation: the <u>mobile</u>
<u>phase</u> and the <u>stationary phase</u>.

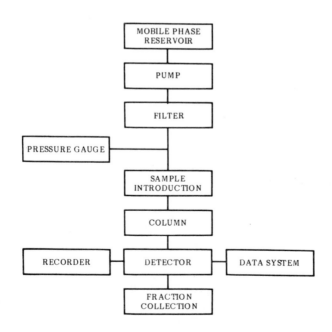

*Fig. 1-3. Functional schematic of a modern
liquid chromatographic system.*

1.51 THE MOBILE PHASE

Except size-exclusion, the mobile phase usually plays an active part in a liquid chromatography system. This is one of the most important differences between liquid and gas chromatography where the mobile phase has no role in the separation process. Thus, the proper selection of the mobile phase is one of the most important decisions when setting up the parameters of a LC separation.

In liquid chromatography, we may use a single substance as the mobile phase during an analysis of the mixture of two or more substances, to properly adjust the characteristics of the phase. Also, one may maintain a constant mobile phase composition during analysis or change it. The first mode is called isocratic operation, while the second is the so-called gradient elution.

Gradient elution is utilized if the sample components have widely different polarity and thus, a change in the polarity of the mobile phase is preferred during analysis in order to improve the separation of later eluting components. Usually, but not necessarily, one starts with a single substance and increases the concentration of the other mobile phase component(s) in time. The change may be linear or follow various non-linear patterns. Figure 1-4 illustrates the possibilities of various gradient elution patterns while Figure 1-5 represents the functional schematic of the system providing the mixed mobile phase to the column.

The selection of the liquids used as the mobile phase depends on a number of parameters. In adsorption and partition chromatography, the polarity plays the most important role, but the viscosity and characteristics which may influence the function of the detector (e.g. UV absorption, refractive index) are also important. In ion-exchange chromatography, the ionic strength (pH) is important while in size-exclusion chromatography the prime consideration is the solubility of the sample in the mobile phase.

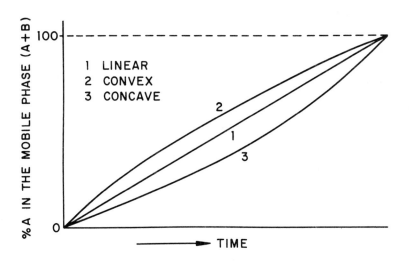

Fig. 1-4. The three possibilities of changing the mobile phase composition in gradient elution.

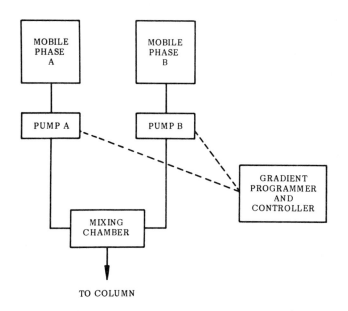

Fig. 1-5. Functional schematic of a system for gradient elution.

Table 1-2 lists the most frequently used mobile phases and column packings (stationary phases).

TABLE 1-2. THE MOST FREQUENTLY USED COLUMN PACKINGS (STATIONARY PHASES) & MOBILE PHASES.

MODE	STATIONARY PHASE	FUNCTIONAL SURFACE	COMMON MOBILE PHASES	TYPICAL APPLICATIONS
ADSORPTION / NORMAL PHASE	Silica gel	$\overset{OH}{-Si}-O-\overset{OH}{Si}-$	Hexane, chloroform, isopropanol	Ethers, esters, porphyrins, mycotoxins oil-soluble vitamins
	Alumina	$Al-O-Al$	Hexane, chloroform, isopropanol	Amines
BONDED PHASES / NORMAL PHASE / PARTITION	Amino	$-NH_2$	Hexane, chloroform, isopropanol	Sugar, steroids, nitro-compounds
	Cyano	$-CN$	Hexane, chloroform, isopropanol	Nitro compounds, amino acids
	Diol	Glycidoxy-ethyl-methoxy silane	Water, 0.1M Na_2HPO_4	Proteins, peptides, aqueous surfactants
BONDED PHASES / REVERSED-PHASE / PARTITION	RP-2	Dimethylsilane	Water, acetonitrile, methanol	Amines, phenols, water-soluble vitamins
	RP-8, C-8	Octylsilane	Water, acetonitrile, methanol	Catecholamines, steroids, essential oils
	RP-18, ODS	Octadecylsilane	Water, acetonitrile, methanol	Analgesics, phthalates, polynuclear aromatics

TABLE 1-2 CONTINUED

MODE	STATIONARY PHASE	FUNCTIONAL SURFACE	COMMON MOBILE PHASES	TYPICAL APPLICATIONS
ION EXCHANGE	Strong cation-exchanger	Sulfonic acid	$0.01-0.1M$ Na_2HPO_4	Water-soluble vitamins, purines, amino acids, nucleosides
	Strong anion-exchanger	Quaternary amine	$0.01-0.1M$ Na_2HPO_4	Nucleotides
	Weak anion-exchanger	$-NH_2$	$0.01-0.05M$ H_3PO_4	Food dyes, carbo-hydrates
SIZE EXCLUSION	Aqueous gel	Sulfonated divinyl-benzene	Water	Proteins, peptides, sugar
	Organic gel	Divinylbenzene	Chloroform, tetra-hydrofuran	Polymers, rubbers
	Controlled-pore silica	Silica gel	Tetrahydrofuran, alcohols, water	Polymers, biological compounds
	Controlled-pore glass	Porous glass	Tetrahydrofuran, alcohols, water	Biological compounds

1.52   THE STATIONARY PHASE

As in any chromatographic process, separation in
liquid chromatography is accomplished through
interactions between the sample and the stationary phase. Thus, its proper selection represents
a key decision in liquid chromatography.

The stationary phase may be a porous solid such
as used in adsorption, ion-exchange and size-
exclusion chromatography. These differ in chemical
composition, structure and particle size. Another
possibility is to use a liquid stationary phase,
as in gas chromatography, and coat it on the
surface of support particles. However, today, such
columns are infrequently used because it is
difficult to prevent the stationary phase from
being washed off the column by the flowing mobile
phase. To prevent this, the mobile phase must be
presaturated with the stationary phase, but its
presence in the eluent is a potential source of
problems in detection or subsequent analysis of
collected fractions.

Today, the most widely used packings in liquid
partition chromatography have the stationary phase
chemically bonded to support particles. These are
the so-called bonded phases which are very durable
and require no conditioning or presaturation of
the mobile phase. Bonded phases are prepared by
chemical reaction between the surface hydroxyl
groups of silica particles and a linear organic
molecule or an organosilane.

Although polar bonded phases, e.g., having an
amino or cyano group at the end of a hydrocarbon
chain also exist (and are used in the normal mode),
the most widely used bonded phases are nonpolar
in nature, with an alkyl chain (e.g., octadecyl)
bonded through the silicon atom of the alkylsilane.
These phases are used in the reversed-mode and are
useful in the separation of a wide range of
substances.

Two types of support particles are used in the
preparation of bonded phases (or as supports to be
coated with a liquid chromatography phase). The
first type is porous through its whole body while

in the second type, there is a solid core with a thin porous skin. The latter is called a <u>pellicular</u> support.

The totally porous support particles generally consist of silica gel with a high surface area. They are available in a wide variety of particle sizes. Pellicular supports consist of a solid core, mostly glass beads, coated with a thin porous layer, usually silica. These are more regular in shape; columns can be packed easily with such material and they operate at low backpressure. However, they are available only in relatively large sizes, and therefore, columns are not as efficient as the more recently available small-particle, totally porous packings.

As already mentioned, the particle size is very important since the mobile phase and the dissolved sample does not diffuse readily, and therefore, the packing particles must be as small as practical to approach the ideal condition where the sample is exposed to the maximum amount of packing surface. There is, however, a lower limit. Below about 3 μm diameter, the particles begin to pack so tightly that liquid cannot readily be pumped through the column. Most commercially available columns now contain packings with average particle sizes of from 5 to 15 μm, while most pellicular packings are available in the range from 37 to 42 μm.

1.53   MOBILE PHASE FLOW CONTROL

Various types of pumps are used in liquid chromatographic instrumentation. They can be classified according to the function which is regulated: either the inlet <u>pressure</u> or the mobile phase <u>flow</u> is controlled. The former provides constant pressure while the latter provides constant flow during operation.

Flow rates are frequently changed in liquid chromatography. The faster the flow, the more rapid the movement of the sample through the system. However, since there is almost no sample diffusion inside the column, low flow rates are generally selected, because efficiency increases as the flow decreases.

Typical flow rates are 1-2 mL/min when 2-5 mm ID columns are used.

In high performance liquid chromatography, high inlet pressures are generally used because of the high pressure resistance of the column filled with very small particles (see below). The more tightly packed the column (and the more viscous the mobile phase), the higher the pressure.

Pressure increases linearly with flow and is some-times a major consideration when flow rates are to be changed. However, pressure is a passive parameter in LC. Pressure itself does nothing to help the system. Typically, the reverse is true. At high pressures, more leaks develop, injection is difficult, and efficiency is lower because the liquid becomes more dense and mass transfer rates are reduced.

All LC pumping systems have a maximum pressure capability. It is unfortunate that this is often considered as the major criterion when evaluating a HPLC system although the best pumping systems may not be the ones with the highest pressure rating. Actually, most work is done at relatively moderate pressures. Table 1-3 lists some typical pressures needed with various columns, packings, and mobile phases to achieve a given flow rate (1 mL/min).

1.54 SAMPLE INTRODUCTION

Sample introduction can be accomplished in various ways. The simplest method is injection with help of a micro-syringe through a septum. Such sample introduction, however, has its problems following mainly from the high pressure of the mobile phase. Therefore, in more sophisticated LC systems, sampling devices are incorporated where sample introduction is done with the help of valves of various construction.

In liquid chromatography, liquid samples may be injected directly and solid samples need only be dissolved in some solvent. The solvent need not be the liquid used as the mobile phase, but fre-quently is judiciously chosen to avoid detector

Table 1-3.   Typical Pressures Needed with Various
Columns, Packings, and Mobile Phases for a 1 mL/min
Flow.

PARTICLE SIZE μm	COLUMN I.D. mm	MOBILE PHASE	MOBILE PHASE VISCOSITY $mPa.s*$	TYPICAL mPa	PRESSURES lb/in^2
5	4.6			10-15	1450-2175
10	2.6	Water	1.00	10-12	1450-1740
10	4.6			2.5	290-725
37	2.6			0.5-2	72.5-290
5	4.6			3-5	435-725
10	2.6	n-Hexane	0.33	3-4	435-580
10	4.6			0.7-1.6	101-232
37	2.6			0.2-0.7	29-101

* 1 mPa.s = 1 cP

The metric unit of pressure measurement dictated
by the International Scientific Committee SI (Sys-
tème International d'Unités) is the pascal abbre-
viated as Pa. One pascal is equal to one newton
per square meter (N/m^2) and, in previously used
units, to 1×10^{-5} bar.

To express commonly experienced pressure units
more conveniently, most scientists use the terms
kilopascal $(kPa = 10^3 Pa)$ or megapascal $(MPa = 10^6$
Pa) Since 1 bar equals 0.9869 atm, 14.5038 psi
and $1.0197 kg/cm^2$, one megapascal equals 10
bar, 9.869 atm, 145.038 psi and $10.197 kg/cm^2$.

interference, column/component interference, or
both. In most cases, it is best to remove solids
from the sample by filtering, decanting, or
centrifuging since continuous injections of solid
particulate material may cause blockage of injection devices or columns.

Samples need not be especially soluble in the
mobile phase. Since, in LC, temperatures rarely
exceed 70°C and the sample is protected from
excessive contact with column tubing, etc., by
being highly diluted in the mobile phase, it is
rare for sample decomposition to occur. Deriv-
itization is sometimes used, but in most cases,
this is to improve detection (permitting the
detection of smaller amounts or making selective
detection possible) and not to protect samples
from decomposition.

Sample sizes may vary widely. The availability of
highly sensitive detectors frequently allows use
of the small samples which yield the highest
column performance. Typical sample sizes with
2.6 mm ID columns range from the nanogram level
up to about 2 mg, depending upon detector sensitivity and the resolution required. In general,
it will be noted that much less sample preparation is required in LC since unwanted or inter-
fering compounds, or both, may often be extracted,
or eliminated, by selective detection.

1.55   COLUMNS

Typical LC columns are 25-50 cm long and are
fitted with extremely small diameter (5-15 µm)
particles. The internal diameter of the columns
is usually between 2 and 5 mm; this is considered
the best compromise among sample capacity, mobile
phase consumption, speed and resolution. However,
if pure substances are to be collected, larger
diameter tubes may be needed. It has also been
found that highest efficiency is obtained when
the column tubing has extremely smooth, polished
inner walls. For this reason, it is normal for
chromatographers who pack their own columns to
purchase special grades of tubing specified for
LC column use.

Packing of the column tubing with the very small
diameter particles requires high skill and special-
ized equipment. For this reason, it is generally
recommended that all but the most experienced
chromatographers purchase prepacked columns, since
it is difficult to match the high performance of
professionally packed LC columns without a large
investment in time and equipment.

In general, LC columns are fairly durable and
one can expect a long service life unless they are
used in some manner which is intrinsically destructive, as for example, with highly acidic or basic
eluents, or with continual injections of 'dirty'
biological or crude samples. It is wise to inject
some test mixture (under fixed conditions) into a
column when new, and to retain the chromatogram.
If questionable results are obtained later, the
test mixture can be injected again under specified
conditions. The two chromatograms may be compared
to establish whether or not the column is still
useful.

When not in use, and disconnected, it is prudent
to use end caps on the columns to prevent drying
out and to store the columns away from sources of
heat and vibration. If the column is used at
elevated temperatures, it is advisable to cool it
to ambient before removing.

After extended use of a column, a baseline drift
may develop. The cause for this is probably the
gradual elution of strongly retained compounds
from earlier injections. These may be washed out
of the column by flushing with a mobile phase
strong enough to remove everything from the system.
In adsorption and reversed-phase chromatography,
it is normal to purge with several hundred milli-
liters of methanol. In ion-exchange chromatography,
the use of a buffer 10 times stronger than that
being used for elution is recommended, as well as
a methanol flush, if there is any chance that the
contaminants may not be water soluble.

1.56   COLUMN TEMPERATURE

The column may be used at ambient or elevated
temperature. Although temperature may be used to
achieve, or control the separation process as is
done in gas chromatography, this is not the primary
reason for using elevated temperatures. In liquid
chromatography, these are used mainly for four
reasons:

● to reduce mobile phase viscosity in order to
achieve lower backpressures and to increase
mass transfer;

- to increase the solubility of the sample in a bonded phase to obtain higher overall system efficiency;

- to increase the ionic migration rates in ion-exchange systems in order to obtain more frequent (thus more) exchange per unit of column length; and

- to increase the solubility of the sample in the mobile phase when marginal, in order to permit the introduction of adequate sample size.

Usually temperatures of 50-70°C are sufficient to achieve these goals.

Independently of the fact, however, whether elevated temperatures are needed or not, temperature control is desired in many cases because the performance of a number of columns is affected by as little as 2-4°C changes at ambient.

1.57 DETECTORS

Today, optical detectors are used most frequently in liquid chromatographic systems. These detectors pass a beam of light through the liquid stream as it passes through a low volume (approximately 10 µL) flowcell. The variations in light intensity caused by UV absorption, fluorescence emission, or change in refractive index (depending on the type of detector used) resulting from the interference encountered as sample components pass through the cell, are monitored as changes in the output voltage. These voltage changes are recorded on a strip chart recorder and frequently are fed into an integrator or computer to provide retention time and peak area data.

The most commonly used detector in LC is the ultra-violet absorption detector. A variable wavelength detector of this type, capable of monitoring from 190 to 800 nm, will be found suitable for the detection of almost all samples.

If UV detectors are used at maximum sensitivity settings, it may be advantageous to keep the detector on overnight to avoid excessive warmup periods. Otherwise, the instruments may be completely turned off overnight. If the instrument remains ON, it is advisable to provide a minimum flow (0.05 - 0.2 mL/min) to avoid potential reaction of solvent-entrained impurities in the UV-illuminated flowcell.

1.58   QUALITATIVE AND QUANTITATIVE ANALYSIS

As in any chromatographic method, qualitative analysis (peak identification) is carried out primarily with the help of the retention times, comparing them to data obtained when analyzing known standards under identical conditions. This is not always sufficient and other additional inform-ation may also be needed. One of the useful aspects of liquid chromatography is that the spectroscopic detectors (UV absorption, fluorescence emission) provide the possibility of identification of the separated components e.g., by tuning to a charac-teristic wavelength or preparing certain derivatives of the sample components and, in most cases, this can be done on-line without the need of fraction collection.

If unknown, and particularly, natural samples are analyzed, one must be very careful to avoid any interferences (erroneous peaks) , the source of which can usually be traced back to plastic containers or tubes with which the sample was in contact during collection, preparation or storage. For example, in serum analyses, the storage of blood in polyvinyl chloride transfusion bags, use of "vacutainer"-type stoppers, use of some makes of collection tubes, and the use of serum separators may inadvertently introduce volatile interferences into the sample that are carried all the way through the final extract. Such interferences may have a detrimental effect on two aspects of the analysis when retention time corresponds with that of a compound of interest, or with that of an internal standard. The former situation will produce false positives and inaccurate quantitation, while the latter will cause inaccurate quantitation. Interferences with LC analysis may be intensified when many compounds are analyzed in a single run.

Due to the possibility of such interferences, it is recommended that blank analysis are performed with the solvents, tubes, pipettes, etc., to be

used with the samples to determine whether they
introduce undesired contaminants to the chromatographic analysis.

Another source of interference may be the components of previous analyses which remained on the
column. Therefore, it is sometimes useful during
an analysis to increase the eluent strength
through a gradient program to assure that no
sample components are retained by the column.

Quantitative analysis is based on peak area values.
It is however, important to realize that the
detector response can vary widely, much more than
is common in gas chromatography (except the
electron-capture detector). For instance, in a
1:1 mixture, it is possible for the detector to
have a response differing by decades for the two
components. Thus, proper calibration under the
conditions of analysis is very important.

Part Two:
The Basis of Liquid Chromatography

As in the past, some of the basic elements of chromatographic theory frequently used in liquid chromatography will be described. As with the material discussed in other chapters, the information includes only those aspects of interest to the practical chromatographer. Detailed discussion of chromatographic theory is available in the basic textbooks; some of them are listed in Table 2-1.

TABLE 2-1

BASIC TEXTBOOKS ON LIQUID CHROMATOGRAPHY

B.L. Karger, L.R. Snyder and C. Horvath: An Introduction to Separation Science. Wiley-Interscience, New York, 1973.

R.P.W. Scott: Contemporary Liquid Chromatography. Wiley-Interscience, New York, 1976.

P.A. Bristow: LC in Practice. HETP Publishers, Handforth, Wilmslow, Cheshire, 1976.

C.F. Simpson: Practical High Performance Liquid Chromatography. Heyden & Son, Ltd., London 1976.

R.J. Hamilton and P.A. Sewell: Introduction to High Performance Liquid Chromatography. Chapman & Hall, London, 1978.

J.H. Knox, J.N. Done, A.T. Fell, M.T. Gilbert, A. Pryde and R.A. Wall: High Performance Liquid Chromatography. Edinburgh University Press, Edinburgh, 1978.

H. Engelhardt: High Performance Liquid Chromatography. Springer, Berlin, 1979.

L.R. Snyder and J.J. Kirkland: Introduction to Modern Liquid Chromatography. Wiley-Interscience, New York, 1979.

C. Horvath: High Performance Liquid Chromatography - Advances and Perspectives. Vol. I-II. Academic Press, New York, 1980.

The text of this part deals with liquid chromatography. However, chromatography has an unified
theory and thus, most of the information discussed here can be applied equally well to the other
versions of chromatography.

2.1 THE SEPARATION PROCESS

As explained in the definition of chromatography
in Chapter 1.1, during a run, the sample molecules
are carried by the mobile phase through the bed of
stationary phase. During this travel, the individual
sample molecules are retarded by the stationary
phase, depending on the interaction between the
individual sample components, the mobile and the
stationary phases. This retardation is selective
which means that, with a given mobile/stationary
phase system the amount of retardation will be
different for each sample component.

In order to understand the separation process, we
shall first investigate one single sample component.
For the sake of simplicity, we call this the solute.

If we inject this sample component into the mobile
phase stream at the top of the column, it will
eventually emerge at the other end. If there would
be no interaction, the solute molecules would travel
through the column with the same speed as the mobile
phase. In other words, they would emerge from the
column when the total volume of mobile phase used
from the instant of sample introduction equals the
void volume, or using another term: the interstitial
volume, V_c (the volume filled with the mobile phase)
of the column. However, because of the interactions,
the molecules of a sample component will emerge
later: i.e., more mobile phase volume is needed for
their elution. We call this the retention volume,
V_R, of the solute.

The use of volumes of mobile phase to characterize
the elution of solutes originated in the time of
gravity-flow liquid column chromatography when there
was no control of the flow rate and when the eluted

fractions were collected volumetrically. However, in modern liquid chromatography, precise-delivery pumps are used to deliver the mobile phase in specific units of volume per period of time (i.e., with a constant flow rate) and time-actuated or time-monitoring measuring devices are used to record the separation. Therefore, today, it is common to think in terms of time instead of volume. Thus, instead of the retention volume, we use the retention time, t_R, and instead of the interstitial volume, we use the mobile phase-holdup time, t_M, the time needed for the mobile phase molecules to travel from the front to the end of the column with the given flow rate.*

The solute is applied at the front of the column as a very narrow band. While it is being eluted from this end to the other, the solute band broadens. This process is due to a number of reasons mainly related to the slowness of the equilibrium process between the two phases and to longitudinal diffusion. Due to this band spreading, while the concentration of the solute in the initial band (i.e., in the injector) was uniform, it now follows (ideally) a normal distribution profile. As a result of this, recording concentration vs time at column outlet, the peak obtained has the form of a Gaussian curve.

Let us assume that we have a sample consisting of two components. The first is inert in respect to the stationary phase; in other words, during their passage through the column, the first component's molecules always remain in the mobile phase and travel at its velocity. The second sample component shows the usual chromatographic behavior interacting with the stationary phase. If we look at the chromatogram obtained by detecting the substances emerging from the column (see Figure 2-1), we shall see two peaks, the first (A) belonging to the "inert" compound while the second (B) to the solute proper.

---

*This is sometimes called the "solvent front", again a leftover from the time of classical liquid chromatography.

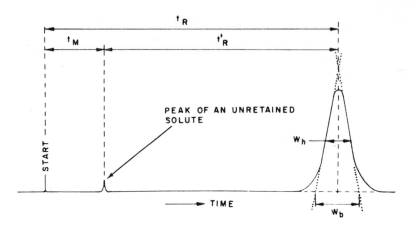

Fig. 2-1. A typical chromatogram.

The retention time of the solute can be divided
into two parts, t_M and t_R. These can be explained
in the following way. During their passage through
the column, the solute molecules spend part of
their time in the mobile phase and the other part
in the stationary phase. While in the mobile phase,
they travel with its velocity, but while in the
stationary phase, they are static: they are
retarded by the stationary phase. Thus

$$t'_R = t_R - t_M \qquad (1)$$

represents the time the solute molecules spend in
the stationary phase. We call this the adjusted
retention time.

When a multicomponent sample is analyzed, each
sample component will spend the same time in the
mobile phase, but - assuming that they are
separated - each will spend a different amount of
time in the stationary phase. This is the reason
for their separation.

2.2 CAPACITY FACTOR (CAPACITY RATIO)

From this point of the chromatographic process,
it is important to know how many times longer the
solute is retarded by the stationary phase than
it spends in the mobile phase because this value

is an indication of how long each component can
be retained on the column. Since t'_R expresses
the time the solute is retarded by the stationary
phase and t_M represents the time it spends in the
mobile phase, their ratio would give this value.
This is called the capacity ratio or capacity
factor:

$$k = \frac{t'_R}{t_M} = \frac{t_R - t_M}{t_M} \qquad (2)$$

There is some confusion in the symbol used to
express this value; unified nomenclatures recommend the symbol k while a number of researchers
pioneering in HPLC, used k' to express the same
term. Following the advice of the unified nomenclatures, we shall use k in this book to express
the capacity ratio.

Let us take an example for the calculation of the
capacity ratio values. In the chromatogram, we
have four peaks - the first representing the
unretained peak. The chart speed is 10 mm/min,
thus it is easy to calculate the various retention
time values corresponding to the individual peaks.
However, since k is a dimensionless value, we can
directly use the distances measured in the chromatogram without first converting them to values in
time units.

Here are the measured retention distances:

Unretained peak:	13.9 mm =	83.4 sec
Peak A	32.5 mm =	195.0 sec
Peak B	69.4 mm =	416.4 sec
Peak C	80.2 mm =	481.2 sec

From these, we can calculate the capacity ratio
values:

Peak A $\qquad \dfrac{32.5 - 13.9}{13.9} = 1.34$

Peak B $\qquad \dfrac{69.4 - 13.9}{13.9} = 3.99$

Peak C $\qquad \dfrac{80.2 - 13.9}{13.9} = 4.77$

Knowing the capacity ratio, we can calculate the retention time of a compound:

$$t_R = t_M (1 + k) \qquad (3)$$

In practice, one should strive to achieve a capacity ratio of at least one for the first peak of interest to assure that it is separated from the solvent and its potential impurities which frequently elute at or close to t_M, and not to have peaks higher than $k = 10\text{-}15$ because the analysis time would be too long. Also, the peak width increases with increasing capacity ratio making resolution and detection difficult.

2.3 CHARACTERISTICS OF THE CHROMATOGRAPHIC PEAK

Let us now go back to the chromatographic peak which, as already mentioned, ideally corresponds to a normal distribution curve. Such a curve is usually characterized by its standard deviation, σ The peak width, at any point, can be expressed as a multiple of the standard deviation. Figure 2-2 indicates characteristic peak widths; from these three are useful:

● w_b, the peak width at base which is obtained by drawing tangents to the inflection points and measuring the length cut out by them from the baseline;

● w_h, the peak width measured at 50% of the total height of the peak ("peak width at half height"); and

● w_i, the peak width measured at the inflection points i.e., at 60.7% of the total height of the peak ("peak width at inflection points").

Since each peak width is a function of the standard deviation, they can also be related to each other, for example

$$w_b = 1.699 \; w_h \qquad (4)$$

$$w_b = 2 \; w_i \qquad (5)$$

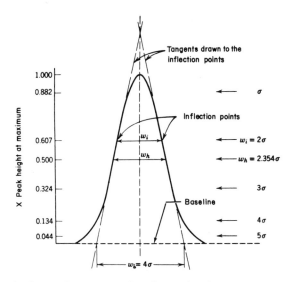

Fig. 2-2. Characteristic widths of a Gaussian peak.

When measuring manually the peak width from a chromatogram, it is very important to consider the width of the recorder pen tracing. Figure 2-3 shows incorrect and correct ways how peak width may be measured with help of a magnifying glass having an engraved scale.

The other two characteristic values of the chromatographic peak are its area and height. The peak area i.e., the integral under the peak, is proportional to the amount (or concentration, depending on the way of detection) of the solute and is

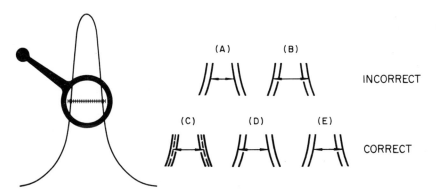

Fig. 2-3. Incorrect and correct measurement of peak width.

thus, used for the quantitative evaluation of the
chromatographic analysis. The peak height is measured to the maximum of the peak and hence corresponds to the highest concentration in the zone.
By definition, retention times are measured to
this point (Figure 2-1). The peak height is proportional to the peak area and thus, in ideal
cases (or, as an approximation) can also be used
for the quantitative evaluation of a chromatogram.
Since, however, a chromatographic peak corresponds
only in ideal cases exactly to a Gaussian distribution curve, peak area values are preferred for
this purpose.

2.4 PLATE NUMBER AND PLATE HEIGHT

From this point of chromatographic separation, it
is important to try to reduce band spreading in
the column as much as possible. After all, if the
peaks are broader, less peaks can be placed in
the same time period in the chromatogram and thus,
less sample components can be separated. On the
other hand, if the peaks are sharper, more peaks
can occupy the same part of the chromatogram and
thus, more sample components can be separated in
a given time. In other words, the sharpness of the
chromatographic peaks is an indication of how good
a column is.

The peak width (i.e., the standard deviation) is
an indication of peak sharpness. However, its
value alone is dependent on a number of parameters
among them e.g., the flow rate. Thus, it is better
to consider a relative value to express peak
quality. The ratio of the standard deviation to
the retention time, or the relative standard
deviation,

$$\sigma/t_R$$

seems to be a good expression. However, it would
be too small a value and, therefore, impractical.
Thus, we should consider its reciprocal, t_R/σ. In
fact, this value had been used by a number of
scientists for this purpose. In practice, however,
another expression, the square of this fraction

$$n = (t_R/\sigma)^2 \qquad (6)$$

has become the accepted expression of column
efficiency. The reason for using the second power
is theoretical and is related to the fact that
from the mathematical standpoint, not the standard
deviation (σ), but its square, the variance (σ^2)
is the basic measure of normal distribution. The
value n is called the plate number or the number
of theoretical plates.

In practice, the plate number is calculated by
using one of the peak widths which can be measured directly from the chromatogram. Substituting
the proper expressions from the equations in
Figure 2-2, the plate number can be expressed as:

$$n = 16 \left(\frac{t_R}{w_b}\right)^2 \qquad (7)$$

or

$$n = 5.545 \left(\frac{t_R}{w_h}\right)^2 \qquad (8)$$

Eq. (8) represents the most widely used form for
the plate number.

The plate number depends on column length: the
longer the column, the larger the plate number.
Therefore, another term has also been introduced
relating the plate number to column length. This
is the plate height or the height equivalent to
one theoretical plate, HETP, the dimension of which
is length:

$$h = \frac{L}{n} \qquad (9)$$

Both the plate number and plate height are terms
used in distillation calculations where each
condensation/evaporation stage was said to occur
on a new level or plate which was an actual tray
in an ascending distillation column. In chromatography, the plates are not real, but are theoretical assessments of the number of partitioning
(distribution) steps the sample molecule under-
goes as it passes through the column.

The lower the plate height and the higher the
plate number, the more efficient the chromatographic column. Let us, for example, take two

25 cm x 2.6 mm ID columns on which the same solute is analyzed. On column A, we measure a distance of 69.4 mm on the chart paper from the start point to peak maximum; with a chart speed of 10 mm/min this corresponds to t_R = 416.4 s. The width of this peak measured at half height on the chart paper is 1.7 mm or, in time units, w_h = 10.2 s. The corresponding values on column B are:

t_R = 80.2 mm = 481.2 s and w_h = 2.2 mm = 13.2 s

The plate numbers are:

$$n_A = 5.545 \left(\frac{416.4}{10.2}\right)^2 = 9241$$

$$n_B = 5.545 \left(\frac{481.2}{13.2}\right)^2 = 7369$$

Each column is 25 cm long; thus, the plate heights are:

$$h_A = \frac{250}{9241} = 0.027 \text{ mm}$$

$$h_B = \frac{250}{7369} = 0.034 \text{ mm}$$

These data show that column A is more efficient.

Extra-column Effects. When speaking about band broadening, one assumes no serious influence of the connecting tubes and the detector cell. Naturally, some longitudinal diffusion (and chance band broadening) will also happen there, but in a properly designed system with adequate mobile phase velocity, the influence will be insignificant. However, with low flow rates and scaled-down column diameters, one may reach a point where systems designed for regular columns and flow rates may not be adequate. Also, even with the usual systems, the user must be careful not to use fittings, connections, or detector cells which are designed for different kinds of analytical parameters.

It is important to emphasize these points because as a consequence, it often happens that a column is blamed for poor performance although it is not the column, but extra-column effects which result in relatively poor performance.

2.5 SEPARATION AND RESOLUTION

Up to now, we only investigated the situation with one peak (besides the peak of the nonretained solute). However, in chromatography, we are analyzing multi-component samples and thus, the separation of the individual components is of prime importance.

Figure 2-4 shows a chromatogram consisting of the peak of the nonretained solute plus two peaks emerging close to each other. Regardless of the number of components in a sample, the problem encountered can always be related to the peak pair most difficult to separate. Thus, we must investigate the separation of two adjacent peaks. This can be expressed in two ways: the first describes their position relative to each other, while the other indicates the degree of resolution.

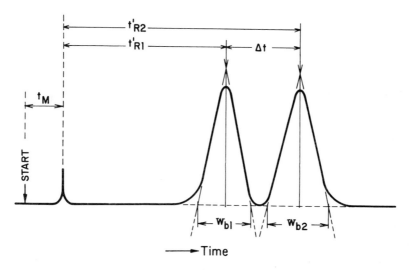

Fig. 2-4. Values measured from a chromatogram containing two closely spaced peaks.

2.51 SEPARATION FACTOR (RELATIVE RETENTION)

The separation factor or relative retention, α, describes the relative position of two adjacent peaks. For its calculation the adjusted retention times are used because the separation of the peaks depend on the selective interaction with the stationary phase i.e., the time they spent in this phase and not on the time they simply travelled along the column with the speed of the mobile phase. Thus, for peaks A and B,

$$\alpha = \frac{t'_{R(B)}}{t'_{B(A)}} = \frac{k_B}{k_A} \qquad (10)$$

Note that the value characterizing the <u>later</u> peak is always placed in the numerator to assure a value of 1.0 or higher for the separation factor. Naturally, if $\alpha=1$ then the two peaks have identical retention times, in other words, there is no separation.

To use the previous example illustrating the calculation of the capacity ratio:

t_M = 83.4 sec

$t_{R(A)}$ = 195.0 sec $\qquad t'_{R(A)}$ = 195.0-83.4= 111.6 sec

$t_{R(B)}$ = 415.4 sec $\qquad t'_{R(B)}$ = 416.4-83.4= 333.0 sec

$t_{R(C)}$ = 481.2 sec $\qquad t'_{R(C)}$ = 481.2-83.4= 397.8 sec

Thus the separation factors are:

$$\alpha_{B/A} = \frac{333.0}{111.6} = 2.98$$

$$\alpha_{C/B} = \frac{397.8}{333.0} = 1.19$$

It will be much more difficult to separate the second peak from the third than the second peak from the first.

The separation factor is a very important value because on a given column with a given mobile phase and at a specified temperature, its value will be the same regardless of the instrument used. This is the basis of qualitative analysis with chromatography. If one peak is specified

and serves as the standard, then the separation
factors of the other peaks relative to this one
can be tabulated. In this context, the separation
factor is usually termed the relative retention.
If an unknown sample (to which the compound being
used as the standard has been added) is now
analyzed under identical conditions (column, mobile
phase, temperature), then individual peaks can be
tentatively identified based on the agreement of
the relative retention values.

As we have seen earlier, the separation factor
(relative retention) is calculated as the ratio
of the two adjusted retention times and not the
retention times. The reason for this is that when
comparing the characteristic retention of columns
(stationary phases), one should only consider the
value related to the retardation process by the
stationary phase. However, when using modern data
systems, the users are often using for convenience
separation factor (relative retention) values
obtained from the uncorrected retention times.
This is acceptable if the data are used only within the same instrument and the correctness of the
values is frequently checked by analyzing standard
mixtures.

2.52 PEAK RESOLUTION

The separation factor expresses the relative
position of the two peaks, however, it does not
give any information on the actual separation of
the peaks. This depends on the sharpness of the
peaks, i.e., the efficiency of the column. This
is illustrated in Figure 2-5 which shows four
chromatograms. The two peaks have identical separation factor value ($\alpha=1.22$), however, column
efficiencies and hence, peak resolution, greatly
differs.

By convention, peak resolution (R_s or R) is
expressed as the ratio of the distance between
the two peak maxima (Δt) to the mean value of the
peak width at base:

$$R_s = \frac{\Delta t}{\frac{w_{b1} + w_{b2}}{2}} = \frac{2 \, \Delta t}{w_{b1} + w_{b2}} \qquad (11)$$

44

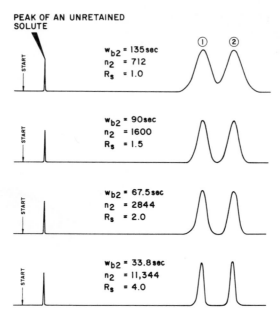

Fig. 2-5. *The influence of column efficiency on peak resolution.*

Constant values: $t_M = 150\ s$; $t_{R1} = 765\ s$; $t_{R2} = 900\ s$;

$t'_{R1} = 615\ s$; $t'_{R2} = 750\ s$; $k_1 = 4.1$; $k_2 = 5.0$; $\alpha = 1.22$.

If resolution is calculated for two closely spaced peaks, then one may assume that the two peak widths are the same. For this case, peak resolution can be calculated from the distance between the two peak maxima and the base width of the second peak:

$$R_s \simeq \frac{\Delta t}{w_{b2}} \qquad (12)$$

A value of $R_s = 1.5$ represents "baseline separation" of the two peaks while $R_s = 1.0$ means that the resolution is about 90% complete. This is enough, in most cases, for peak area calculations.

We have seen earlier that the peak width at base is obtained by drawing the tangents to the inflection points of the two peaks and measuring the distance cut out by the tangents from the baseline. This is a somewhat time-consuming operation

and this is exactly the reason that in plate
number calculation, the use of the peak width at
half height is preferred.

Basically and principally, one may also use w_h in
the resolution calculation; however, the values so
obtained will be different to those obtained
when using eqs (11) or (12).

If we use the symbols of R_b and R_h for resolution
equations- using the peak width at base and half
height respectively - these can be converted into
each other with the help of the following relationships:

$$R_h = 1.699 \ R_b \qquad (13)$$

$$R_b = 0.589 \ R_h \qquad (14)$$

2.6 VELOCITY AND ITS INFLUENCE ON COLUMN EFFICIENCY

Since the solute molecules are carried through the
column by the mobile phase, it is natural that its
speed has an influence on the process in the column.
For example, if the flow rate is too small, the
solute molecules will spend too much time in the
mobile phase where longitudinal diffusion can
increase band spreading. On the other hand, if the
flow rate is too fast, the solute molecules do not
have enough time to interact with all the active
sites of the stationary phase - we may say that
they are swept away before this can happen.

In theoretical discussions, one prefers to express
the speed of the mobile phase flow with its velocity rather than its flow rate. The velocity can
easily be established by measuring the elution time
(t_M) of a unretained solute and divide the column
length (L) by its value:

$$u = L/t_M \qquad (15)$$

The dimension of velocity (u) is length/time and is
usually expressed in units of mm/sec.

From the above discussion, it is clear that there must be an optimum velocity where everything is just right and here the column efficiency must be the best. This is clear if we plot velocity vs. plate height (HETP). Such a plot is shown in Figure 2-6. These plots are called the van Deemter plots named after the prime author of a paper published in 1956 which first discussed the detailed theory of chromatography:

J.J. van Deemter, F.J. Zuiderweg and A. Klinkenberg: Longitudinal Diffusion and Resistance to Mass Transfer as Causes of Nonideality in Chromatography.

Chemical Engineering Science. 5, 271-289 (1956).

There is a significant difference in the velocity and particularly HETP values encountered in present-day modern liquid chromatography as compared to the values common just 10 years ago. Then the minimum of the van Deemter plot represented a HETP of 0.5-1.0 mm while today, values of 0.015-0.02 mm are not uncommon. Also, the slope of the ascending part of the plot after it reached its minimum was much steeper 10 years ago than it is today. This is a very important achievement and is mainly due to developments in controlled porosity, small particle column packings. Of course, a smaller slope means that one can use a higher velocity without too much loss in column efficiency.

The equation describing the van Deemter plot relates column efficiency (HETP) not only to the velocity (u), but also to a number of other parameters such as the capacity ratio, the particle diameters, and the diffusion coefficients of the solute in the mobile and stationary phases. Its study gives important information on the directions one should follow in improving the performance of liquid chromatography. In fact, such studies represented the basis of the evolution of modern high performance liquid chromatography. On the other hand, the individual relationships by the van Deemter equation (the equation related to the plot) are too complex for the practical chromatographer to use in his day-to-day work. Therefore, we are not discussing them here; those who are interested in them are referred to the textbooks listed in Table 2-1.

As seen in Figure 2-6, the van Deemter curve has a minimum where the best column efficiency can be obtained. The velocity corresponding to this optimum is the optimum linear mobile phase velocity. However, little work is done in this region because these velocities are very small, at or below 0.5 mm/sec.

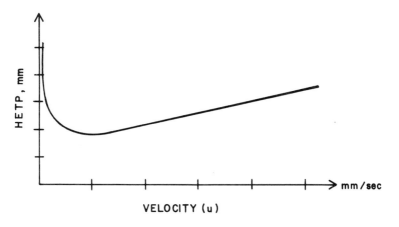

Fig. 2-6. A van Deemter curve.

The usual working velocities are at the 2-5 mm/sec range with the most frequently used 2.6 mm ID columns. This corresponds to a volumetric flow rate of about 0.5-1 mL/min. The relationship between retention time (t_R), velocity (u), column length (L), and the capacity factor (k) is described by the following equation:

$$t_R = \frac{L}{u}(1 + k) \qquad (16)$$

2.7 REDUCED PLATE HEIGHT AND VELOCITY

In many cases in liquid chromatography, instead of using the plate height and mobile phase velocity, as discussed above, the corresponding "reduced" values are used. Although the practical chromatographer probably will not use these in his day-to-day work, a brief explanation is included here because these expressions might be encountered in the literature.

The reduced plate height, h_r, recognizes the fact that the most important contribution to the plate height is the particle diameter. Thus, the reduced plate height expresses the plate height (h, HETP) relative to the particle diameter, d_p:

$$h_r = h/d_p \qquad (17)$$

Thus, we may say that the reduced plate height gives the number of particles per plate.

The reduced mobile phase velocity, ν, takes account of the particle size (d_p) and the diffusivity of the solute in the mobile phase. The speed of molecular diffusion into the pores of the particle can be expressed as

$$D_M /d_p$$

where D_M is the diffusion coefficient of the solute in the mobile phase, the dimension of which is area/time. Thus the reduced mobile phase velocity is the ratio of the flow velocity down the column (u) and the above value:

$$\nu = \frac{u\ d_p}{D_M} \qquad (18)$$

If the two velocities are equal, $\nu = 1$.

Part Three:
The Technique of Liquid Chromatography

After a brief overview of liquid chromatography
and its basic terms and relationships, we shall
now discuss in more detail the technique of
liquid chromatography. This discussion will start
with a summary on the type of column packings
used and a discussion of the most common column
parameters. Subsequently, we shall deal with the
individual modes and then finish by summarizing
the information a chromatographer needs to develop
the chromatographic method best suited to solve
his problem.

3.1 COLUMNS AND COLUMN PACKINGS

The heart of a chromatograph is the column. Thus,
special attention has to be devoted to the material placed in the column tubing (the stationary
phase) and also to the influence of column
parameters on column performance.

3.11 COLUMN PACKINGS

All chromatographic separations are performed on
the stationary phase. The stationary phases in
liquid chromatography are usually silica particles
packed into the column. These particles can serve
as adsorbents in liquid adsorption chromatography
or as supports in partition chromatography. Originally liquid stationary phase coated on these
porous support particles have been used; however,
these are more-or-less replaced by the so-called
bonded phases in which the organic compound used
as the phase is chemically bound to the support
particles. In size-exclusion chromatography, the
particles have precisely defined pore sizes
permitting separation according to molecular size
while in ion-exchange chromatography, chemically
bonded ionic groups on the particles'surface
provide the desired effect.

49

50

The original particles used in liquid chromatography were fairly large (40 μm or more) and
porous in their entire body (see Figure 3-1a).

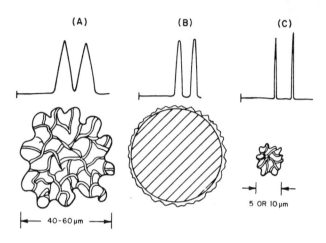

Fig. 3-1. Various types of column packings used in
liquid chromatography: (a) body porous (fully porous),
(b) pellicular, (c) body porous microparticle. The
chromatograms above the particles visualize the peak
broadening.

Such particles have a large surface area, thus,
such a packing has a high surface capacity, i.e.,
can accept a large amount of sample. The drawback is that it may take a different amount of
time for sample molecules to diffuse into and
out of the different pores of the particle
resulting in excess band-broadening.

The first major solution to this problem was
suggested by Horvath: to coat a solid, non-porous
core (e.g., glass bead) with a thin-layer of the
porous phase, e.g., an adsorbent or an ion-
exchanger. In this case, the sample molecules only
migrated through this relatively thin layer,
resulting in much narrower peaks. Figure 3-1b
visualizes this type of particle - the so-called
pellicular packing.

According to the chromatography theory, smaller
particles augment the exchange rate between the
mobile and stationary phases so that sufficiently
low plate heights can be obtained at relatively

high flow velocities. Thus, in the evolution of
chromatography, the goal had been to be able to
produce smaller particles. Here, not only the
smallness of the diameter is important, but also,
the particles must have a fairly uniform diameter
and regular shape. In addition, proper techniques
were also needed to be able to pack these small
particles into the small diameter columns.

The effect of using the small particles is visualized in Figure 3-2. The larger particles leave
relatively large spaces between them. Sample
molecules are flushed rapidly through the void
spaces while similar molecules are being retained
inside the particles. The result is peak-broadening
as shown in the upper graph. At the bottom, the
small particles are seen to pack more tightly and
void volumes are much lower with the resulting
increases in efficiency, as all similar molecules
travel through the column in approximately equal
times. The danger in using too small a particle
is, of course, that the column may become so
tightly packed that liquid cannot be pumped
through it at any practical pressure. This is one
of the reasons why in practice, there is a limit
as to how small the particles should be.

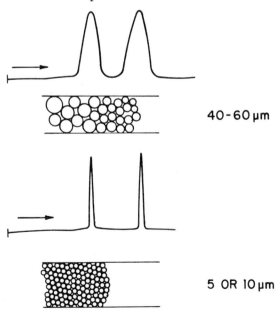

40-60 µm

5 OR 10 µm

Fig. 3-2. The effect of packing diameter on column
efficiency.

Today, as a result of this development, uniform small particle packing is available. The particles have a diameter of 10 μm and, in some cases, even as low as 5 μm; they are again fully porous ('body porous') since, due to the small diameter, inter-particle sample migration is rapid. Figure 3-1c visualizes such a particle. These particles have a high surface and, actually, there is even more surface available per equal column length; thus, their sample capacity is better.

Microparticulate packings are not restricted to body-porous materials and pellicular packings are also available in 10-μm particles. Since the inner particle migration time is even more reduced, these packings can provide very high efficiencies. However, their sample capacity is smaller than that of the body-porous materials and these pack-ings are, at least at this moment, very expensive.

Table 3-1 summarizes the various column packings, their advantages and disadvantages.

3.12 COLUMN DIMENSIONS

3.121 COLUMN DIAMETER

The liquid chromatographic columns generally used in practice have internal diameters of either 2-2.6 or 4.6-5 mm. One should be careful with catalogue values because they are often rounded off; thus, a nominal 5 mm ID might be 4.6 mm. The actual selection depends on many things. The smaller diameter columns use less mobile phase and permit the detection of smaller concentrations in the sample even though the total sample capacity of these columns is less. The reason for this is that the concentration of the sample component in the volume of mobile phase* corresponding to its band (peak) is higher because the latter is reduced by

---

*The volume of mobile phase corresponding to a chromatographic peak is calculated by convention as the volume corresponding to the peak width at half height. Thus, if w_h is expressed in minutes and the flow rate, F_c, in mL/min, then the corresponding volume is $F_c w_h$.

Table 3-1. Types of HPLC Packing Materials.

PARTICLE DIAMETER μm	PARTICLE SHAPE	TYPE	ADVANTAGES	DISADVANTAGES
40 - 60	irregular	body-porous	inexpensive low backpressure	poor efficiency
40	regular	pellicular	easy to pack low backpressure	medium efficiency low capacity
5 - 13	irregular	body-porous	high efficiency high capacity	difficult to pack higher backpressures
10	regular	pellicular	high efficiency relatively easy to pack moderate back-pressure	low capacity expensive
10	regular	body-porous	high efficiency moderate back-pressure moderate to high capacity	relatively expensive difficult to pack

a factor larger than the reduction in the sample size. Thus, these considerations would prefer the smaller diameter columns. On the other hand, due to the smaller absolute sample capacity, the smaller diameter columns are unfavorable if sample collection is desired e.g., in order to analyze the collected fraction by other techniques such as IR, NMR or mass spectrometry. When this is necessary, the largest weight of sample possible must be chromatographed. Since sample loading capacity is a function of the amount of packing material present, a larger diameter column is preferred: e.g., a 4-6 mm ID column contains over three times more packing material than a 2-2.6 mm ID column.

The influence of column internal diameter on efficiency is different from that in gas chromatography. In GC, smaller diameter columns (with appropriately reduced particle sizes) generally have a higher efficiency for the same length i.e., smaller HETP. This is, however, not always so in liquid chromatography: until the recent advent of packing materials with very small (less than 10-μm) particle sizes, it had been generally noted that use of columns with very small cross sections resulted in decreased efficiency. The reason for this is not theoretical, but is connected to the packing technology.

Though some use of 1 mm columns had been reported, most high efficiency work is being done in columns having a bore of 2 mm or larger. In fact, several recent observations have shown that as column diameter is increased, as long as the mobile phase flow rate is increased to provide the same linear velocity,* separating efficiency may improve.

A possible explanation of all these observations is that in a very narrow column too much

---

* For example, if we have a flow rate of 0.64 mL/min on a 2.6 mm ID column, we need a flow rate of a mL/min on a 4.6 mm ID column to maintain the same velocity.

unpacked space, through which the sample travels freely without undergoing partition, exists around the wall of the column and this "open volume" contributes greatly to peak broadening. Naturally, this "wall effect" also exists in larger diameter columns, however, there, the relative proportion of packed cross section to the area corresponding to this open volume is higher, particularly when particles with very small (5-10 µm) diameter are used where even most of the wall area becomes tightly packed.

Naturally, the logical conclusion of all these considerations is that if even smaller diameter packing particles will be commercially available, column diameter will probably be further reduced.

Another contribution to the loss in efficiency when using narrower diameter columns most likely comes from the sample size. Naturally, one has to correspondingly reduce sample size when column diameter is reduced, but there is a general tendency of trying to inject higher sample volumes than is really permitted. This is also con- nected to detector limitations; there is certainly a lot of possibility for further improving the sensitivity of our present-day detectors. If more sample is injected (to be able to see components present in small concentrations) than column capacity would permit, then naturally, the columns will be overloaded and efficiency reduced.

Above, we mentioned that the influence of diameter in LC on column efficiency is different than in GC. Another difference is that even for prepara- tive work, one is not selecting a too-large diameter column; even for the injection of rela- tively large samples (1 g and higher) columns with 7-14 mm ID (3/8-5/8 inch O.D.) are used. There are a number of reasons for this, the major being expense; the packing in a 1 in. OD x 50 cm long preparative column is probably worth several thousand dollars! An important secondary reason for the use of smaller diameter preparative columns is the problems associated with the ques- tion of supplying, pumping, and disposing of the large amounts of high-purity liquids required to operate wide diameter columns.

3.122   COLUMN LENGTH

Commercially available columns for liquid chromatography are usually 25 cm long. If more theoretical plates are necessary than such a column
could provide, usually two or more such columns
are connected in series. The main reason that
this is preferred to a single longer column, is
related to the technique of column packing; it
is much more difficult to prepare a longer than
a shorter high-efficiency column. Thus, two or
three shorter columns properly connected in series
will actually have a higher overall efficiency than
a single column of comparable length.

In gas chromatography, column connection is generally avoided because the "dead volume" of the
connector can easily be detrimental to column
efficiency. The situation is somewhat different
in liquid chromatography; here, the mobile phase
is a liquid instead of a gas and the diffusion
is much slower in a liquid than in a gas. Thus,
column connection without significant band
spreading can be accomplished.

3.2   SEPARATION MODES

There are four traditional separation modes in
liquid chromatography:

> liquid-solid (adsorption) chromatography
> liquid-liquid (partition) chromatography
> size-exclusion chromatography and
> ion-exchange chromatography

More recently, ion-pair chromatography (specific
combinations of the ion-exchange and partition
modes) has been established as another principal
mode.

During the early stages of the development of
modern liquid chromatography, extended research
had been carried out on the development of partition chromatography with liquid stationary phases
similar to the gas chromatographic system. However, the development of bonded phases significantly simplified this mode and thus, today, when

speaking about liquid partition chromatography, almost exclusively bonded phases are considered.

In addition to this grouping, we may also divide the liquid chromatographic techniques according to the nature of the mobile phase. If we consider its polarity relative to the stationary phase, two modes can be specified: the so-called normal ("forward") phase chromatography where the stationary phase is more polar than the mobile phase and reversed-phase chromatography where the opposite is true. We may also consider the composition of the mobile phase: if it is constant during a run, we speak about isocratic elution while, if it is changed during the run, the technique is called gradient elution. Since reversed-phase chromatography and gradient elution are very important modes of operation in liquid chromatography used in the majority of the analyses performed today, we shall deal with them separately.

Usually with any given column type, one of the principal modes will predominate in the separation mechanism. However, in any given mode there is often some contribution from more than one mechanism. For example, with a silica gel column, the separation mechanism is essentially adsorption; however, the use of mixed solvents as the mobile phase usually leads to some partitioning effects. Size exclusion can also occur with silica columns. With ion-exchange and size-exclusion column packings, adsorptive effects can occur which modify the separation. Bonded-phase partition column packings also are believed to involve a considerable amount of adsorption in their separation mechanism. Thus, it can be seen that the exact mechanism of separation in any given instance is often difficult to determine. However, this need not interfere in the selection of a separation system based on a logical consideration of the sample properties, since it is the separation we are concerned with - not the mechanism. An exception is in the size exclusion mode where molecular weight distributions are desired. In this case, steps must be taken to assure that only size exclusion is occurring. The choice of separation mode is usually fairly simple after a general knowledge of the sample has been gained.

In the subsequent chapters, we shall discuss separately the individual separation modes.

3.3 LIQUID-SOLID ADSORPTION CHROMATOGRAPHY

3.31 PRINCIPLES

Liquid-solid adsorption chromatography is usually best-suited to the separation of compounds having different polarities. This polarity of the molecules arises from the presence and/or position of different functional groups in the molecules.

Table 3-2. Functional Groups Involved in Adsorption Chromatography.*

FUNCTIONAL GROUP	STRUCTURE
Methyl	$-CH_3$
Fluoro	$-F$
Chloro	$-Cl$
Nitro	$-NO_2$
Aldehyde	$-CHO$
Acetyl	$-O-\overset{O}{\overset{\|}{C}}-CH_3$
Hydroxy	$-OH$
Keto	$-\overset{O}{\overset{\|}{C}}-$
Amino	$-NH_2$
Carboxyl	$-COOH$
Amide	$-NH_2$

* In approximate order of increasing adsorption affinity.

Some typical functional groups are shown in Table
3-2 and are listed in order of increasing polar
effect. In general, if a molecule has more than
one functional group, the most polar one will
have the major effect and will determine the
elution time required. For this reason, adsorption
chromatography often separates mixtures into
classes of compounds, the classes being determined
by the most polar functional group(s) in the
compounds.

Since silica gel is by far the most widely used
adsorbent, we shall explain the principles of
adsorption chromatography considering this material
as the stationary phase.

The adsorption mechanism can be visualized most
easily by considering the process as the establishment of an equilibrium inside the column. A
mobile phase (acetone in Figure 3-3, but usually
a mixture of several liquids) is chosen which has
a polarity approximately equal to (or slightly
weaker than) that of the sample. A sample molecule
(the 'amine' in Figure 3-3) which is adsorbed to
a hydroxyl group on the packing surface is being
continuously bombarded by the moving stream of
mobile phase molecules. This physical flushing
weakens the sample-to-packing bond, allowing the
constant stream of almost equally-charged sample
molecules to dislodge the sample and move it downstream to the next available OH group where its
slightly higher polarity allows it to dislodge
resident mobile phase molecules. It can readily
be seen that the greater the number of these
successive steps or stages, the greater are the
chances that sample components having slightly
different charges may spend greater or lesser
amounts of time in the column and thus become

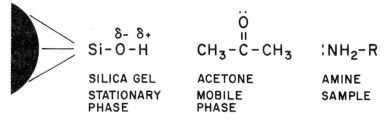

Fig. 3-3. The adsorption mechanism.

separated. These steps are approximated numeri-
cally as 'theoretical plates' (see Section 2).
Columns having a high number of plates can be
seen to provide better separations than those
with low plate numbers.

3.32 ADSORBENTS

Liquid-solid adsorption chromatography is most
frequently carried out using either silica gel or
alumina as the stationary phase (column packing).
Other adsorbents such as charcoal, Florisil,
calcium carbonate, etc., have been used, but have
limited importance for normal applications in
modern liquid chromatography.

Since the most frequently used adsorbent is silica
gel, further discussion will be limited to it.

3.321 SILICA GEL

For high performance liquid chromatography, silica
gel is generally available as fully porous ('body
porous') particles, or as spherical glass beads
which are coated with a thin surface layer of
irregularly shaped silica gel (the so-called
'pellicular' silica gel). These packing types have
been described earlier.

The surface of the silica gel of either type is
covered with Si-OH and Si-O-Si groups which can
interact with the sample molecules. From these,
the surface hydroxyl groups are the most important.
As indicated by Figure 3-4, two types exist: free
hydroxyls (OH) with energy levels of about
7 Kcal/mole, and reactive hydroxyls (HOH) which
exhibit about 13 Kcal/mole bonding energy. The
latter represents very strong bonding agents which
may permanently adsorb polar sample components and
which adsorb water onto the gel. This double
activity is often responsible for wide, or split,
peaks and nonreproducible results.

The reactive hydroxyls may be deactivated by the
addition of water or an alcohol (ethanol or
isopropanol) to the column or by using a mixed
mobile phase containing water, or preferably, an
alcohol. There are also other methods to permanent-

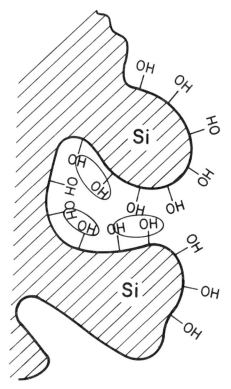

Fig. 3-4. Free and reactive hydroxyl groups on the surface of silica.

ly deactivate the reactive hydroxyls by chemical reaction and such packings are used widely in practice.

Deactivated silica gel is preferred in the separation of very polar compounds such as e.g., alcohols, amines or acids. However, for samples of low polarity or for nonpolar compounds such as e.g., hydrocarbons, nonmodified silicas are preferred.

It should be mentioned that if deactivation is carried out by the addition of water or using a water-containing mobile phase, the amount of water permanently bonded to the silica surface depends very much on the conditions such as e.g., room temperature. Similarly, nondeactivated silica may also adsorb water from the atmosphere and again, its amount depends on room temperature and air humidity. This uncontrolled amount of water may result in poor retention time reproducibility. This is the reason why it is preferable to use an alcohol as the surface-modifying agent or a silica gel where surface modification was carried out by chemical reaction.

The permanently adsorbed water also contributes to the separation process: it can act as a liquid stationary phase and thus, the separation will be the result of combined adsorption and partition process.

3.322 PARTICLE SIZE AND PORE SIZE

When selecting an adsorbent as column packing, the size of the particles and pore must be considered.

The particle size is important for several reasons. The smaller the average particle size, the higher will be the surface area, and hence, the activity. In addition, for a given length of column, the smaller the particle size of the packing, the higher the efficiency of the column; but also, the higher its backpressure. For best results, very narrow particle size distributions must be used since 'fines' can plug up a column and raise its backpressure.

While some pressure is always needed to force the liquid through the column, pressure is not in itself an advantage. If an analysis can be done using 200 psig, there is no advantage in going to 1000 psig, all other things being equal. Materials of particle size smaller than 20 μm, such as silica A/10 and B/5 are difficult to hand-pack into columns and is best obtained in factory-packed columns. Larger particle size material is easy to hand-pack, is moderately efficient, and gives very low back-pressures.

The pore size of the silica gel should be sufficiently large to allow easy entrance and exit of the sample molecules. Too small a pore size leads to lower activity because of the size exclusion effects.

3.33 THE MOBILE PHASE

3.331 THE POLARITY OF THE MOBILE PHASE

The selection of mobile phase in liquid adsorption chromatography is most conveniently done with the help of the so-called Hildebrand scale listing the solvent strength parameter, $\varepsilon°$, of various liquids used as the mobile phase. Table 3-3 presents this scale for selected liquids.

The $\varepsilon°$ values are relative to pentane for which $\varepsilon°$ is defined as equal to zero. These values were originally measured by Hildebrand in 1932, but the scale was put into its most useful form by Snyder in his basic book which should be consulted by anybody interested in adsorption chromatography and particularly in its theory:

> L.R. Snyder: Principles of Adsorption Chromatography. M. Dekker, Inc., New York, 1968.

Table 3-3 is compiled according to Bristow who further expanded Snyder's table.

These values were originally obtained by measuring the heat generated as each solvent was adsorbed onto alumina. The more active the solvent, the higher the level of heat (or bonding energy). Thus, we see nonpolar solvents such as simple alkanes listed at the top with zero, or almost zero, energy; chlorinated solvents in the center; and alcohols and water with their highly active hydroxyl groups, down near the bottom.

Although the values were measured on alumina, the activity is generally identical (or uniformly slightly lower) on silica gel and thus, the scale can also be used well with silica gel. The only exception is tetrahydrofuran which has a value of $\varepsilon° = 0.62$ on silica gel.

Other useful data are also included in Table 3-3 such as viscosity. Since the pressure is a linear function of viscosity, the higher the viscosity, the higher the pressure. There is no benefit from pressure beyond the 100-200 pounds used to actuate

Table 3-3. Properties of Substances Used as Mobile Phase.*

SUBSTANCE USED AS THE MOBILE PHASE	ε°	VISCOSITY, cP AT 20°C	REFRACTIVE INDEX	UV CUTOFF** nm
Fluoroalkanes	-0.25	0.39	1.267	210
1,1,2-Trichlorotrifluoro-ethane		0.69	1.356	230
n-Pentane	0.00	0.23	1.358	210+
2,2,4-Trimethylpentane (isooctane)	0.01	0.50	1.404	210+
n-Hexane	0.01	0.33	1.375	200+
Cyclohexane	0.04	1.00	1.427	210+
Cyclopentane	0.05	0.47	1.406	210
1-Pentene	0.08	0.24	1.371	215
Carbon disulfide	0.15	0.37	1.626	380
Carbon tetrachloride	0.18	0.97	1.466	265
m-Xylene	0.26	0.62	1.500	290
Di-n-propyl ether	0.28	0.37	1.368	220
2-Chloropropane	0.29	0.33	1.378	225
Toluene	0.29	0.59	1.496	285
1-Chlorobutane	~0.30	~0.35	1.397	225
Chlorobenzene	0.30	0.80	1.525	

SUBSTANCE USED AS THE MOBILE PHASE	ε°	VISCOSITY, cP AT 20°C	REFRACTIVE INDEX	UV CUTOFF** nm
Benzene	0.32	0.65	1.501	280
Bromoethane (ethyl bromide)	0.37		1.424	
Diisopropyl ether		0.33	1.368	220
Diethyl ether	0.38	0.23	1.353	220
Ethyl sulfide	0.38	0.45	1.442	290
Chloroform	0.40	0.57	1.443	245
Methylene chloride	0.42	0.44	1.424	235
Tetrahydrofuran	0.45	0.55	1.408	215
1,2-Dichloroethane	0.49	0.79	1.445	225
Methyl ethyl ketone	0.51	0.40	1.381	330
1-Nitropropane	0.53	0.84	1.400	380
Acetone	0.56	0.32	1.359	330
Dioxan	0.56	1.54	1.422	220
Ethyl acetate	0.58	0.45	1.370	260
Methyl acetate	0.60	0.37	1.362	260
1-Pentanol	0.61	4.10	1.410	210
Dimethyl sulfoxide	0.62	2.24	1.478	
Aniline	0.62	4.40	1.586	
Diethyl amine	0.63	0.38	1.387	275

SUBSTANCE USED AS THE MOBILE PHASE	ε°	VISCOSITY, cP AT 20°C	REFRACTIVE INDEX	UV CUTOFF** nm
Triethyl amine		0.38	1.401	
Nitromethane	0.64	0.67	1.394	380
Acetonitrile	0.65	0.37	1.344	190
Pyridine	0.71	0.94	1.510	305
Dimethoxyethane		0.45	1.380	220
1,2-Dichlorobenzene (ODCB)		1.32	1.552	
1,1,2-Trichloroethylene		0.57	1.476	
N,N-Dimethylformamide		0.92	1.428	
Tetrachloroethylene		0.90	1.505	
N-methylpyrrolidone		1.65	1.470	
1-Methylnaphthalene			1.618	
Dimethylacetamide			1.438	
Decahydronaphthalene, trans (decalin)			1.470	
Trifluoroethanol	0.74	~1.20	1.219	
2-Methoxyethanol		1.72	1.401	220
2-Propanol	0.82	2.30	1.380	210+
Ethanol	0.88	1.20	1 361	210+
Methanol	0.95	0.60	1.329	205+

SUBSTANCE USED AS THE MOBILE PHASE	ε°	VISCOSITY, cP AT 20°C	REFRACTIVE INDEX	UV CUTOFF** nm
1,2-Ethanediol	1.11	19.90	1.427	210+
Acetic acid	large	1.26	1.372	
Water	large	1.00	1.330	

* Data taken from the table published in P.A. Bristow: LC in Practice, hetp, Inc., Wilmslow, 1976. Listing is in increasing solvent strength ($\varepsilon°$). For additional data on these solvents, see Table 3-10.

** Wavelength at which the liquids become opaque in ultra-violet.

+ Extremely good grades may be used as low as 195-190 nm. Manufacturers of substances for liquid chromatography use continuously improve the purity of the individual solvents; thus, it may be possible that in the most recent trade literature, lower values are listed.

68

check valves or compress seals. At high pressure, leaks are more likely to develop, molecules become more dense (reducing mass transfer), and injection techniques become more difficult.

The scale also includes information which is useful in selecting mobile phases to be compatible with the detector available to the analyst. If a refractive index detector is used, liquids are chosen to have the largest possible refractive index difference between sample and mobile phase. When UV is used, the solvents with low UV cutoff become most useful. Several of these with cutoffs around 210 nm are also available in higher states of purity with even lower cutoffs, to make far UV detection practical.

The most frequently used liquids are <u>hexane</u>, <u>isooctane</u>, butylchloride, chloroform, <u>methylene chloride</u>, tetrahydrofuran, <u>acetonitrile</u>, iso and n-propanol, <u>methanol</u> and <u>water</u>. From these, those underlined are available in higher purity permitting lower UV cutoffs. With the help of these liquids, blends can be made to provide mobile phases in almost any polarity range.

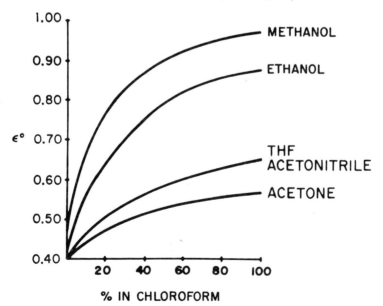

Fig. 3-5. *Polarity values, expressed as* $\varepsilon°$*, of binary mobile phases with chloroform as the common component. THF = tetrahydrofuran.*

3.332 MIXED MOBILE PHASES

Since the adsorption process involves competition
for active sites on the support, addition of even a
small amount of a more polar liquid selectively
fills many sites, creating a rapid increase in
effective mobile phase polarity. In Figure 3-5,
for example, the change in the $\varepsilon°$ values when
adding a more polar liquid to chloroform is
presented. It can be seen that a 10% addition of
methanol to chloroform yields a polarity increase
of about 0.25 $\varepsilon°$ units. Even smaller polarity
changes can significantly change the separation.

For example, Figure 3-6 shows the effect of the
addition of 1% THF to chloroform. The mixed

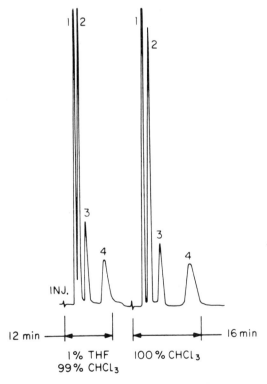

Fig. 3-6. Effect on resolution resulting from small
changes in mobile phase polarity.
Column: 50 cm x 3 mm ID, packed with Sil-X silica
gel; particles: 37 μm, totally porous.
Mobile phase flow: 1 mL/min. UV detection at 254 nm.
Peaks: 1 hexachlorophene, 2 butylated hydroxyanisole,
3 methyl prednisolone, 4 methyl paraben.

mobile phase is slightly more polar than pure
chloroform and thus, the separation of hexachlorophene and butylated hydroxyanisole is
better in the less polar phase. One needs a polar
mobile phase to elute these polar compounds from
the column; however, if the mobile phase is too
polar, then it will compete with the sample
molecules for the stationary phase active sites
thus reducing the separation of the sample components.

In this example, the less polar phase was preferable; in the next sample, Figure 3-7, the opposite is true. Here aromatic alcohols are analyzed
on a nondeactivated silica. If pure n-hexane is
used as the mobile phase, the sample components
remain adsorbed on the stationary phase. Adding
only 0.5% acetonitrile to make the mobile phase
slightly polar permits elution of all three components in a little over 30 minutes, while doubling
the acetonitrile percentage reduces the analysis
time to about 17 minutes.

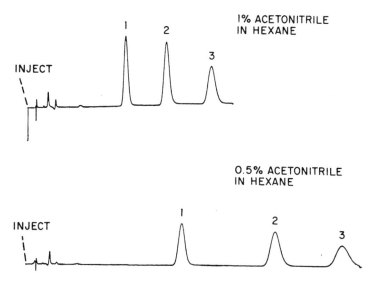

*Fig. 3-7. Effect on resolution resulting from small
changes in mobile phase polarity.
Column: 50 cm x 2.6 mm ID, packed with Silica B/5;
particles: 5 μm, totally porous.
Mobile phase flow: 1 mL/min. Column temperature: 50°C.
Peaks: 1 1-phenylethanol, 2 benzylacohol, 3 3-phenyl-
propanol-1.*

This dramatic change in adsorptive energy experienced when small amounts of polar materials are allowed to mix with less polar or non-polar liquids, points out the care required in the exact dosing of the small concentration component and also illustrates the care required when changing mobile phases and modes of chromatography. In order to avoid contamination of the new mobile phase by traces of the previously used one, pumps, plumbing, and injection systems must be completely flushed before work with the new mobile phase can be commenced. Since many of the solvents used in HPLC as mobile phases must be of the highest purity, the expense involved in solvent change-over may become considerable. For this reason, it is important that in instrument design, this question is considered by selecting the proper flow geometry so that the volume of new solvent needed to purge the system can be kept as low as possible.

Although, naturally, it is possible to use a pre-mixed mobile phase in the liquid chromatograph, in practice, mixing is usually done in the instrument, by delivering the pure components and combining the flows prior to the injection port valve. It is obvious that in such a case, repetitive analyses are highly dependent on the reproducibility of the mixing techniques or instruments used. For example, in case of dual-head reciprocating pumps, the flow rate may fluctuate as a function of check valve actuation when the pumps are called on to deliver less than 0.1-0.4 mL/min (depending on the particular pump/check valve design). This implies that if e.g., a dual pump system is used to deliver a binary mobile phase at a total flow of 1.0 mL/min the pump providing the lower concentration (usually the more polar) component may be erratic if this component is to be only a small concentration of the total flow. As a result, retention times, especially those of early-eluting solutes, may vary.

This problem can be avoided by diluting the less-polar component with a portion of the more polar component and filling the reservoir of the pump delivering the more polar component with this mixture. Figure 3-8 shows an example of how a 2%

isopropanol-in-n-hexane mobile phase can be prepared in the instrument.

This technique is a good practice to follow even when using high precision pumps, since it provides more flexibility in cases when minute changes in the concentration of the strong component are required. For example, if we want to change the concentration of isopropanol in the example shown in Figure 3-8 to 2.1%, we simply change the respective flows to 0.42 and 0.58 mL/min, by dialing 42%A and 58%B instead of 40%A and 60%B.

Isopropanol/hexane mixtures have proven very useful for general adsorption chromatography. The UV cutoff is much lower than that experienced when the chlorinated solvents which were commonly used in the past are employed, and this single mixture covers a wide polarity range (a 10/90 isopropanol/hexane mix has an $\varepsilon°$ of about 0.65).

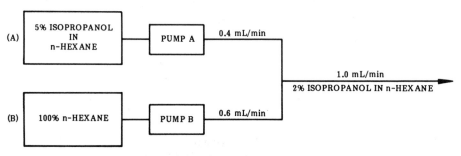

Fig. 3-8. Preparation of a binary mobile phase in the liquid chromatograph.

3.4 PARTITION CHROMATOGRAPHY

3.41 CLASSICAL LIQUID-LIQUID PARTITION CHROMATOGRAPHY

Classical liquid-liquid chromatography involves the partition of the sample components between a liquid stationary phase and the liquid mobile phase. The separations occur due to differences in the solubilities of the sample components in the two liquid phases. The liquid stationary phase is coated on the particles of a solid support.

The two liquids used as the stationary and mobile phase respectively, must be almost totally immiscible and each must be saturated with respect to the other. For this reason, the combinations used usually represent a non-polar mobile phase such as hexane with a very polar stationary phase such as poly(ethylene glycol) or β,β'-oxydiproprionitrile (ODPN). However, since liquids which are practically immiscible will usually still have at least ppm solubility in each other, the hexane must be pre-saturated with the polar phase to prevent gradual column stripping and loss of separating power.

Figure 3-9 illustrates a typical example for partition chromatography. Separation occurs by the acetophenone molecules partitioning between the hexane mobile phase and the ODPN film. Since acetophenone is more soluble in the latter than in hexane, it will be retained by the stationary phase for a longer period of time.

Figure 3-9 is an example for normal (forward) phase chromatography where the stationary phase is more polar than the mobile phase.

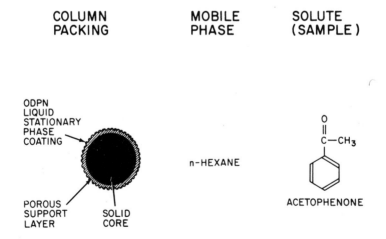

COLUMN PACKING   MOBILE PHASE   SOLUTE (SAMPLE)

ODPN LIQUID STATIONARY PHASE COATING

POROUS SUPPORT LAYER   SOLID CORE

n-HEXANE

ACETOPHENONE

Fig. 3-9. Example for liquid partition chromatography having the stationary phase present as a thin coating on porous support particles. Usually, pellicular supports are used for this purpose.

It can be seen that if the solute is too soluble
in the stationary phase and not very soluble in
the mobile phase, it may not be eluted from the
column. It then becomes necessary to modify the
mobile phase by adding a more polar, i.e.,having
higher solubility for polar molecules, component
to the hexane. This new mixture must be pre-
saturated with ODPN since the ODPN will be even
more soluble in the new mixed mobile phase than
it was in hexane.

It becomes apparent that this type of chromatography can be troublesome and time-consuming
since presaturation steps require heating and
stirring, sometimes for hours, to acquire
equilibrium. In addition to this, the presence of
stationary phase in the eluent can interfere with
detection and can contaminate collected fractions.
For these reasons, most modern liquid chromatographers prefer to use bonded-phases.

3.42 BONDED PHASES

Because of the problems listed above, column
packings have been developed in which the stationary phase is permanently bound to the support by
chemical bonding. These materials are called
bonded-phase packings. Although for convenience,
bonded-phases are usually discussed under partition
chromatography, it is now clear that the separation
mechanism, particularly in the case of reversed-
phase chromatography with the alkylsilyl phases
(see below) is not purely partition.

Figure 3-10 shows the structure of the various
bonded-phase types. These are prepared by the
reaction of the surface Si-OH groups of the support
particles with various reagents. Table 3-4 lists
the more frequently used bonded-phase packings;
from these, the one having octadecylsilyl groups -
called the ODS-phase- is probably the most popular.

Some of the bonded-phases such as those with amino,
cyano, or hydroxy groups are polar in nature and
can be used in the same manner as silica and other
adsorbents or polar liquid stationary phases, with
low polarity mobile phases. On the other hand, the
alkylsilyl and phenyl bonded-phases are commonly

used in the reversed-phase mode, with a very polar
mobile phase. This technique will be discussed
below in more detail.

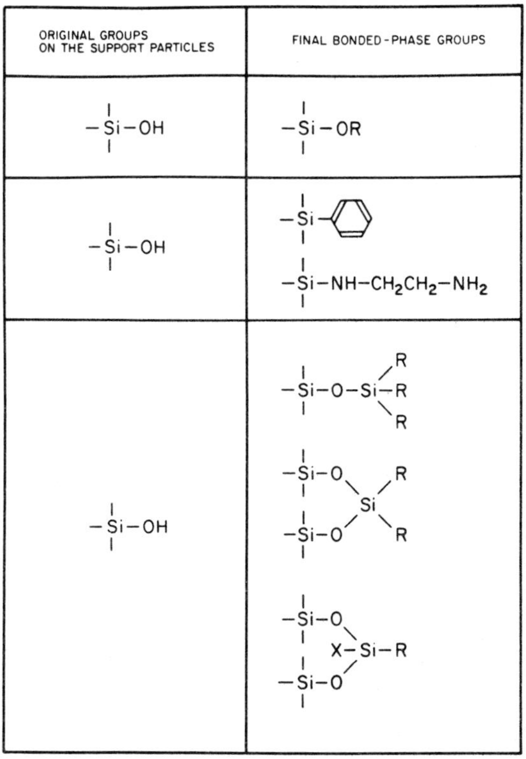

Fig. 3-10.   Typical structures of bonded phases.

Bonded-phase packings in the reversed-phase mode
are most useful with samples which are insoluble
or only moderately soluble in water. Some examples
are aromatic hydrocarbons, oils, steroids,
plastics, polymers, alkaloids, and other high
molecular-weight compounds.

As mentioned, columns with octadecylsilyl bonded-
phase are probably used more today, than any
other type. However, these may be eventually
replaced by bonded-phase columns which have a
shorter, more flexible alkyl chain. Such a material
is C-8 or RP-8 containing octylsilyl groups. These
columns have advantages as compared to ODS columns
for a number of sample types presently analyzed on
ODS packings. Such compounds are glycosides,

Table 3-4. Most Frequently Used Bonded Phases.

MODE	FUNCTIONALITY	STRUCTURE OF BONDED GROUP
Normal phase	AMINO	$-NH_2$
	Cyano (nitrile)	$-CN$
	Diol	$-\overset{\mid}{\underset{\mid}{Si}}-O-CH_2-\overset{\mid}{\underset{OH}{CH}}-CH_2OH$ $-\overset{\mid}{\underset{\mid}{Si}}-O-CH_2-\overset{\mid}{\underset{OH}{CH}}-CH_2OH$ $-\overset{\mid}{\underset{\mid}{Si}}-O-CH_2-\overset{\mid}{\underset{OH}{CH}}-CH_2OH$
Reversed-phase	Dimethylsilyl	$>\!\!Si\!<\!\!\overset{CH_3}{\underset{CH_3}{}}$
	Octylsilyl	$>\!\!Si-CH_2-(CH_2)_6-CH_3$
	Octadecylsilyl	$\geqq\!Si-CH_2-(CH_2)_{16}-CH_3$
	Phenylsilyl	$\geqq\!Si-\langle\bigcirc\rangle-OH$

urinary acids, carboxylic acids, sulfonamides,
thyroid hormones, azo dyes, and many more polar
lipid compounds. Although both phases contain alkyl
chains, there are distinct differences between them.
It is generally agreed that the short octyl surface
shows better selectivity toward the moderately-
polar types of compounds, thus, the octadecyl phase
should be used primarily for non-polar (lipophilic)
samples.

3.5 SPECIAL TECHNIQUES RELATED TO THE MOBILE PHASE

In liquid chromatography, two techniques related
to the selection of the nature and composition of
the mobile phase are widely used. These are
reversed-phase chromatography and gradient elution.

In reversed-phase chromatography, the mobile phase
is more polar than the stationary phase. Today,
this is probably the most widely used mode in
liquid chromatography.

While in all of the previously discussed modes,
the composition of the mobile phase is kept
constant during a run (isocratic analysis), in
gradient elution the composition is changed, thus
providing different polarity effects for the individual peaks. Naturally, gradient elution can be
applied in both the normal and reversed-phase mode.

Below, these two techniques are discussed in more
detail. In addition, information on the possible
use of ternary mobile phase is summarized. This
technique was introduced recently. Its utilization
requires more complicated instrumentation and
programming; however, there are special cases
where it may be beneficial to the chromatographer.

3.51   REVERSED-PHASE CHROMATOGRAPHY

In earlier chapters we have mentioned a few aspects
of reversed-phase chromatography. Today, probably
more than 70% of liquid chromatographic analyses
are carried out in reversed-phase systems. A more
detailed discussion of some of the questions
associated with this mode is given here to aid
the practical chromatographer in obtaining the
maximum benefit from this separation mode. A
typical reversed-phase separation is shown in
Figure 3-11.

3.511 PRINCIPLES

The reversed-phase chromatographic separation
process is explained with the help of Figure 3-12.
Water-methanol or water-acetonitrile mixtures are
typical mobile phases used in this mode. The non-
polar anthracene molecule is soluble in the non-
polar ODS stationary phase and less soluble in
the mobile phase consisting of water-methanol
mixture. Increasing the methanol content of the
mobile phase would increase the solubility of
anthracene in this phase and remove it from the
column more quickly. Conversely, if the sample
elutes too rapidly, the water content is increas-

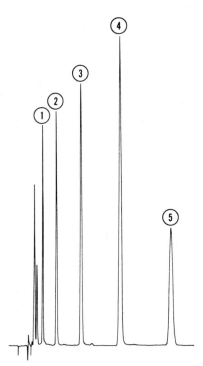

Fig. 3-11. *Typical reversed-phase separation on bonded phase column packing.*
Column: 25 cm x 2.6 mm ID, packed with ODS-Sil-X; particles: 10 μm, spherical, totally porous. Mobile phase: 3:7 acetonitrile-water, flow rate 1 mL/min. Column temperature: 55°C. Peaks: 1 benzene, 2 toluene, 3 ethylbenzene, 4 isopropylbenzene, 5 tert. butylbenzene. Analysis time: 15 minutes.

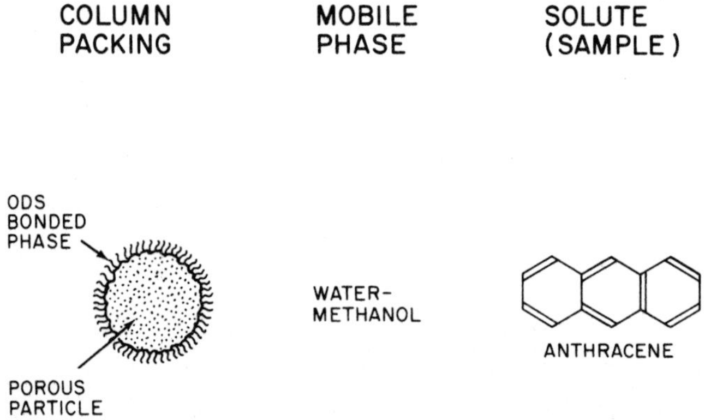

COLUMN PACKING	MOBILE PHASE	SOLUTE (SAMPLE)

ODS BONDED PHASE

WATER-METHANOL

ANTHRACENE

POROUS PARTICLE

Fig. 3-12. *Example for reversed-phase liquid chromatography with nonpolar column packing.*

ed, thereby allowing the sample to be preferentially dissolved in the stationary phase for a longer period of time. Since the stationary phase cannot be dissolved off the support particle, it is also possible to change the concentration of the binary mobile phase during a run; this is gradient elution and will be discussed below.

As mentioned above, the mechanism of separation on bonded phases when running in the reversed-phase mode is certainly not purely partition. In fact, some researchers prefer to call this use reversed-phase adsorption. Others feel that there are at least three separation mechanisms occurring simultaneously: adsorption, partition, and surface tension.

In a basic paper,* Horvath and Melander suggest a possible explanation for the analysts' ability to use reversed-phase columns for the separation of not only the non-polar compounds which follow the traditional "like-dissolves-like" pattern described by the partition theory, but also the separation of moderately and highly polar species such as steroids, alcohols, etc. These latter separations may be accomplished by utilizing the surface tension properties of the packing surface. At high water concentrations, the surface tension forces between sample molecule and stationary phase tend to be high; as more organic modifier is added to the mobile phase, the surface tension bonds are reduced and components are eluted.

3.512 THE MOBILE PHASE

The usual mobile phase in reversed-phase chromatography with bonded phases is a mixture of water and a miscible, less polar solvent such as methanol, acetonitrile, dioxane, tetrahydrofuran, etc. Water is the "weakest" solvent and yields

---

*C. Horvath and W. Melander: Liquid Chromatography With Hydrocarbonaceous Bonded Phases. Journal of Chromatographic Science 15, 393-404 (1977).

the longest retention times. Increasing the concentration of the less polar solvent in the water
decreases retention times. This is illustrated in
Figure 3-13, plotting the retention time of
naphthalene against the concentration of acetonitrile in the binary mobile phase water/aceto-
nitrile.

The actual choice of the less polar component of
the mobile phase is dependent upon a number of
different factors. Of these, the more important
are sample solubility, mobile phase/sample/detec-
tor compatibility, mobile phase viscosity, and
system efficiency. None of these are independently
variable, and the best solvent to satisfy all the
conditions should be chosen.

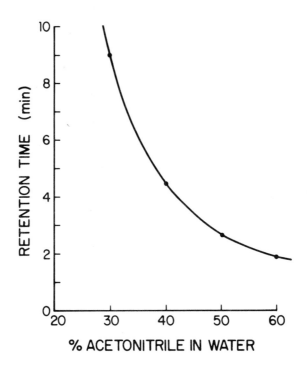

*Fig. 3-13. Dependence of retention time on the
percentage of a less-polar component in an
aqueous binary mobile phase.
Solute: naphthalene. Column: 25 cm x 2.6 mm ID,
packed with ODS-Sil-X; particles: 10 µm, spherical,
totally porous. Mobile phase flow rate: 1 mL/min.
Column temperature: 50°C.*

The mobile phase selected should be one in which
the sample is readily soluble. If far UV detection
is being used, then it should have low UV absorptivity in the region used for detection. Table
3-5 lists the most common substances used as
components of the mobile phase in reversed-phase
chromatography with bonded phases and their UV
cutoffs. It should be mentioned that if one of
the organic substances is used in low concentrations in combination with water, the binary
mixture may be used at a lower cutoff than listed
for the pure substance. For example, in general,
the best mobile phase component to add to water
for detection at 195 nm is acetonitrile; however,
THF/water may be used if THF is present in
low concentrations.

Table 3-5. The Most Commonly Used Mobile Phase
Components in Reversed-Phase Chromatography and
Their UV Cutoffs.

SUBSTANCE	UV CUTOFF nm
Water	<187
Acetonitrile	190
Methanol	205
Tetrahydrofuran (THF)	210
Dioxane	220

Of these common liquids, acetonitrile and aceto-
nitrile/water mixtures have the lowest viscosity,
(see Table 3-3), and thus would be the mobile
phase of choice if the system is pressure limited.
Because of this low viscosity, acetonitrile will
often give the highest efficiencies. Measurements
have shown that an increase of almost 30% in efficiency can be achieved when using acetonitrile as
compared to methanol. Additional problems that are
encountered when methanol/water mixtures are used,
are that there is a positive heat of mixing and
the mixture tends to outgas strongly, a very high
volume contraction, and an abnormal viscosity

curve where a 1:1 mix of the two has a viscosity of about 1.8 cP while the viscosity of pure methanol and water are 0.60 cP and 1.00 cP, respectively. This results in a wide swing in pressure during gradient programs.

When analyzing complex samples, or samples with components having widely differing capacity factor values, gradient elution is often helpful. This technique will be discussed below; here, just a few practical suggestions are given. The mobile phase components are chosen according to the same criteria as in isocratic runs except that the UV characteristics of the individual components must also be considered; there should not be a large difference in their absorbance at the chosen wavelength, otherwise a serious baseline drift will be observed. Experimentation has shown that in general, a slightly convex gradient is most effective in reversed-phase chromatography. Usually the gradient runs from water to acetonitrile or from water with a lower acetonitrile concentration to water with a higher acetonitrile concentration.

When running water-soluble, ionizable samples, it is usually necessary to suppress the ionization of the sample. If this is not done, severe tailing problems will occur. For acidic compounds, it is usually only necessary to add less than 1% of an acid, such as phosphoric or acetic. In the case of gradient elution employing UV detection, the former is preferred to the latter. For basic compounds, the situation is more difficult since it is not possible to use pH's higher than 7.5 on most silica-based columns. For difficult basic compounds, probably the best approach is ion-pair chromatography which will be discussed separately below.

The optimum flow rate for bonded-phase columns is 0.5 - 2 mL/min for the 2.6 mm ID columns and 1-4 mL/min for the 4.6 mm ID columns. Since the van Deemter curve for these columns is very flat, only marginal increases in efficiency are obtained by decreasing the flow rate. They may conveniently be operated at the highest recommended flow rate assuming that they are compatible with the pressure limitations of the instrument.

3.513 COLUMN TEMPERATURE

Temperature is a very important parameter in liquid chromatography, perhaps as important as flow rate or solvent strength. The effects of changing the temperature vary with the mode of chromatography used. In reversed-phase chromatography, four main areas are affected: the solubility and retention time of the sample, the viscosity of the mobile phase, and the efficiency of the column.

In cases where the sample/solvent solubility is poor, as is often the case in reversed-phase chromatography, increasing the temperature will increase the solubility and greatly improve peak shape and efficiency.

Concerning the retention time, the obvious effect of increasing column temperature is to decrease the retention time. Figure 3-14 presents, as an example, the actual relationship for naphthalene on an ODS-Sil-X column. Three conclusions can be drawn from this. First, if the analysis is to be speeded up, this can also be achieved (besides increasing the flow rate) by increasing the column temperature. However, if the flow rate (and hence, the mobile phase holdup time) is kept constant, increase of temperature will decrease the capacity factor which, in turn, has an influence on the column efficiency needed to achieve a given separation: in general, the smaller the capacity factor, the more theoretical plates are necessary for a given separation. Finally, it is obvious that in repetitive analyses, the constancy of column temperature is imperative if retention times are to be reproduced.

The column temperature also affects the viscosity of the mobile phase: it decreases with increasing temperature. With constant-pressure pumps, this results in a decrease in operating pressures (see Figure 3-15). This is particularly important when using high viscosity mobile phases such as the aqueous mixtures employed in reversed-phase work.

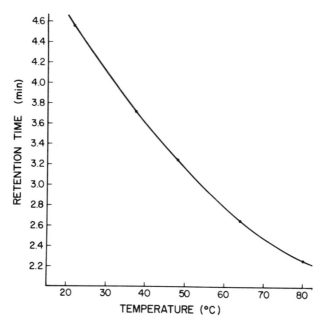

Fig. 3-14. Variation of retention time with column temperature.
Sample: naphthalene. Column: 25 cm x 2.6 mm ID, packed with ODS-Sil-X; particles: 10 µm, spherical, totally porous. Mobile phase: 45:55 acetonitrile-water, flow rate 1 mL/min.

Last, but by no means least, increasing the column temperature will -up to a limit- increase the overall column efficiency. This is due to an increase in the mass transfer of the sample components between the mobile and stationary phases. Figure 3-16 shows this relationship for an ODS-Sil-X column with naphthalene as the sample. This particular curve is fairly shallow; however, on some reversed-phase materials, such as e.g., C-8 packing, the change is more dramatic and raising the temperature from 30 to 60° can double the plate number.

The aforementioned would indicate that one should always use the highest possible temperature. There are, however, two limitations. First, as seen in Figure 3-16, the curve eventually is reaching a plateau where change in the plate number is negligible. Even more important, as discussed above, the capacity factor decreases with increasing

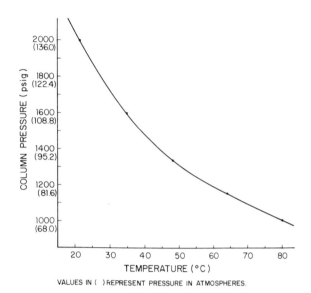

*Fig. 3-15. Variation of column inlet pressure
with temperature.
Column: 25 cm x 2.6 mm ID, packed with ODS-Sil-X;
particles: 10 μm, spherical, totally porous.
Mobile phase: 45:55 acetonitrile-water, flow rate
1 mL/min.*

temperature requiring higher plate numbers for
the same separation, and the latter effect eventually will be more dominant than the first.
Thus, there is a limit how much it is practical
to increase column temperature.

3.52 GRADIENT ELUTION

In Figure 3-17, we see what Lloyd Snyder has
called "the general elution problem". In liquid
chromatography, we think of "solvent strength"
(the polarity of the mobile phase); on the other
hand, in gas chromatography we think of column
temperature. The problem occurs when a sample
contains a variety of components, all of which
cannot be eluted by a single weak mobile phase as
shown at the top of the figure, or which are
incompletely separated if a strong solvent is
used as in the second row. Attempting to use a
blend, we may optimize the center, but both front
and back ends of the chromatogram are unsatis-
factory. It becomes obvious that some more sophis-

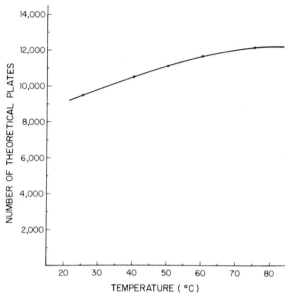

Fig. 3-16.   Variation of column efficiency with
temperature.
Sample: naphthalene. Column: 25 cm x 2.6 mm ID,
packed with ODS-Sil-X; particles: 10 μm, spherical,
totally porous. Mobile phase: 45:55 acetonitrile-
water, flow rate 1 mL/min.
Capacity ratio of naphthalene: 6.5.

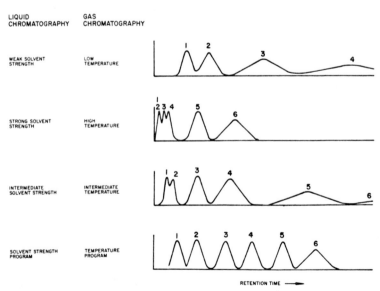

Fig. 3-17.   The general elution problem and its
solution.

ticated method must be used to obtain ideal resolution of all peaks. This is done by beginning with
a weak mobile phase and gradually feeding in a
stronger mobile phase component. This is called
gradient elution.

Before we continue this discussion, we would like
to emphasize an important concept. It is common
in practical liquid chromatography to speak about
weak and strong solvents (mobile phases or mobile
phase components) and thus, we are also using
these terms here although they are misleading
because their meaning depends on the nature of
the stationary phase:

- in adsorption and normal phase chromatography
  where, in general, the stationary phase is
  more polar than the mobile phase, a "weak
  solvent" is less polar than the other mobile
  phase component;

- on the other hand, in reversed-phase chromatography where the mobile phase is more polar
  than the stationary phase, a "weak solvent"
  is more polar than the other mobile phase
  component.

Often gradient elution not only represents an
improvement in separation, it is absolutely necessary to elute all the sample components of the
column. This is illustrated in Figure 3-18: in
isocratic analysis, the fourth component, p-hydroxybenzoic acid, would not come off the column for at
least 30 minutes. On the other hand, if gradient
elution is used starting with 100% isooctane
(2,2,4-trimethylpentane) and continuously adding
chloroform at 5%/min, p-hydroxybenzoic acid will
emerge in the form of a sharp peak in less than
18 minutes.

If percent concentration of component A in the
binary mixture A+B is plotted against time, the
so-called gradient curves specifying the change
in the mobile phase composition during an analysis are obtained. Figure 1-4 already shows the
three possible types. What we are really interested in, however, is the change in the elution
strength of the mobile phase with time. In

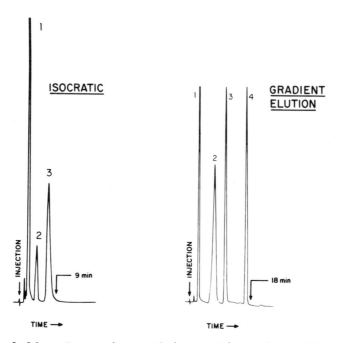

Fig. 3-18.   Comparison of isocratic and gradient
elution analysis.
Column: 50 cm x 3 mm ID packed with Sil-X II
silica gel; particles 40 μm, pellicular. Total
mobile phase flow: 1 mL/min. Left: isocratic,
9:1 isooctane-chloroform. Right: gradient elution,
starting with 100% isooctane and adding chloroform
at 5%/min.
Peaks: 1 4-methoxybenzaldehyde (p-anisaldehyde),
2 3-ethoxy-4-hydroxybenzaldehyde (ethylvanillin),
3 3-methoxy-4-hydroxybenzaldehyde (methylvanillin),
4 4-hydroxybenzoic acid. Sample volume: 1 μL, each
component present at 2 μg/μL.

reversed-phase chromatography with alkylsilyl-
type bonded phases, the two curves are practically the same; however, in adsorption chromatography, they are not. The reason for this is
the shape of the $\varepsilon°$ vs. composition curve which
is convex (see Figure 3-5). Thus, if a linear
elution strength change is desired, a concave
gradient curve must be selected to compensate for
this effect. This is explained with the help of
Figures 3-19 and 3-20.

In Figure 3-19, Curve I presents the change in
elution strength of a n-hexane/chloroform binary

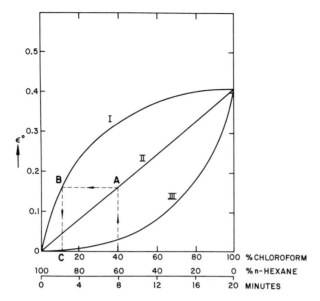

Fig. 3-19. Elution strength plots for a binary
mobile phase. For explanation, see text.

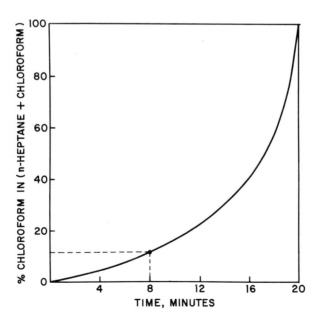

Fig. 3-20. Gradient curve to achieve the linear
increase in elution strength (curve II) in Fig.
3-19.

mobile phase with composition. However, we would like to achieve a linear change corresponding to Plot II. We can obtain this if the gradient curve shown in Figure 3-20 is followed. The curve was obtained by placing a time scale on Figure 3-19 as a second abscissa and establishing for each time instant the actual composition which would give the elution strength corresponding to the respective point on the linear plot. This is explained below with help of one point:

We assume that the complete gradient is obtained in 20 minutes. Thus, we place a 20-min scale below the plots of Figure 3-19. At 8 minutes, the elution strength of the binary mobile phase should be A. This is obtained by drawing a vertical line to the 8-minute point in the new abscissa. To obtain the composition corresponding to this value of $\varepsilon°$, we draw a horizontal line from Point A to Curve I, and at this interception point (Point B), we drop a vertical line to the abscissa expressing the concentration. Point C corresponds to 11% chloroform and 89% n-heptane. Thus, in Figure 3-20, we plot this point.

If we carry out this procedure with a number of points, the curve in Figure 3-20 will be established. Actually, this curve corresponds to Curve III in Figure 3-19, the mirror image of Curve I.

In practice, one does not have to go through such step-by-step establishment of the gradient curve. The instrument instruction manuals provide typical curves which approximate most of the actual situations, and the user only has to select the most appropriate of these.

In general, a linear elution strength change is desired if no special separation problems exist in a particular part of the chromatogram, but the reason for gradient elution is to facilitate the elution of the successive peaks. Convex gradients are used if a number of components are grouped together toward the end of the chromatogram, the separation of which is difficult, while a concave gradient facilitates the separation of earlier peaks.

The actual manner in which gradient elution is carried out in a liquid chromatograph depends on the type of pumps used. In the case of instruments which use single reciprocating pumps, the gradient is produced by the gradual addition of the stronger solvent to the reservoir from which the main pump transfers the mobile phase to the column. Figure 3-21/A represents the flow schematic of such a system. Usually, it is possible to obtain different program rates by varying the speed of the gradient feed pump (pump B).

In more sophisticated, dual-pump systems, the two components are delivered separately to a mixing point and fed from there to the column. The flow schematic of such a system is shown in Figure 3-21/B. The run begins by feeding the weaker component, and the instruments can be programmed to begin feeding the stronger component, typically over a period of 5 to 999 minutes with either linear or infinitely - variable convex or concave curvature, with simultaneous reduction of the weak-component pump flow to maintain a preset constant flow rate to the column.

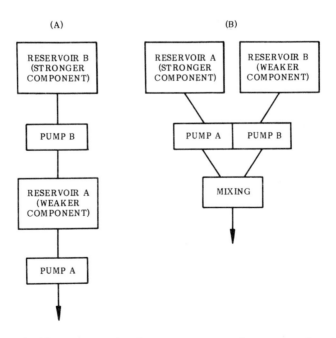

Fig. 3-21. Practical ways to produce a polarity gradient of the mobile phase.

3.53 TERNARY MOBILE PHASES

All of the previous discussions on mixed mobile phases referred to binary mobile phases. Recently, in some cases, several researchers have shown examples of the apparent need for continuous control of the proportional mixing of three eluents, that is, the use of ternary mobile phases. There are two principal types of application where the use of ternary mobile phases may be beneficial.

The first application is related to samples having components with widely different polarity, where the strongly retained components cannot be eluted with any solvent which is miscible with a solvent weak enough to allow separation of the weakly retained sample components. In this case, a gradient program is initiated starting with only the weaker solvent as the mobile phase and an intermediate solvent is slowly introduced to elute moderately retained components; then later, a third, stronger solvent is added to the second.

In practice, this mobile phase profile requires relatively complex programming, especially if the analytical conditions are to be repeated. In most cases, satisfactory elution can be accomplished with binary systems if the stronger solvent is composed of a mixture of the intermediate and the strongest solvents.

The second application is related to the cases when system modifiers are employed as in an analysis where pH control, ion-pairing or ionization suppression is required. In such cases, the capability of the third solvent is used to supply a constant amount of modifier, regardless of the varying concentrations of the two primary solvents. This technique can also be approximated with binary systems where the same amount of modifier is added to each, so long as the modifying agent is soluble in both.

Besides these two principal applications, ternary systems may be advantageous in the development of optimum analytical conditions: time savings may be accomplished if a third solvent is readily available for experimentation or addition to the system. However, once experience has been gained with the column/mobile phase system in use, there is only infrequent need for this sort of random selection. In addition, consideration of the complex effects of dual solvent mixing and subsequent reequilibration may suggest the extra degrees of difficulty involved in successful use of a third solvent in the system.

While the use of ternary mobile phases may achieve some special effects, its proper optimization is a complex task. Also, its use requires fairly complex instrumentation. For these reasons, subsequent discussions on mobile phase selection will only refer to mobile phase consisting of one or two components.

3.6 SIZE-EXCLUSION CHROMATOGRAPHY

3.61 PRINCIPLES

In size-exclusion chromatography, the components of a sample are separated according to the size of their molecules. The technique was originally developed for the separation of biological materials in aqueous media on bead-formed gels consisting of dextran cross-linked with epichlorohydrin, and in this form, was called gel filtration.

A significant breakthrough in the evolution of the technique was its extension to the separation of polymers dissolved in organic solvents, utilizing polystyrene-type beads; this form was known for some time as gel-permeation chromatography (GPC). Since the basis of the two techniques is the same, they are now combined under the name of size-exclusion or simply, exclusion chromatography.

The improvement in column packings also widened the fields of application of size-exclusion chromatography and today, it extends from relatively simple organic compounds to high polymers. Figure 3-22 visualizes the typical samples and the corresponding molecular weight ranges.

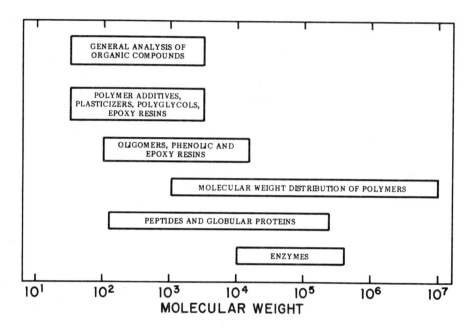

Fig. 3-22. Molecular weight distribution of samples most frequently analyzed by size-exclusion chromatography.

The methods and applications of exclusion chromatography have grown tremendously in the last decade. Once limited to very slow gravity-fed columns packed with soft organic gels, molecular size-exclusion is now capable of rapid, high pressure operation. This new capability is, in large part, due to the development of modern packing materials which have precisely defined pore sizes and which are mechanically strong enough to resist high pressures. Outstanding among these new stationary phases are the rigid divinylbenzene-type gels (Shodex) which may be used for the analysis of either substances soluble in organic solvents or -in sulfonated form- water-soluble compounds. These new packings are available in various grades each covering a discrete molecular size range. By combining columns of different size range, a wide sample molecular weight range can be analyzed.

The size-exclusion column packing behaves, in some ways, like a sieve. This allows the smallest molecules to enter the pores of the packing while excluding the molecules which are larger than the

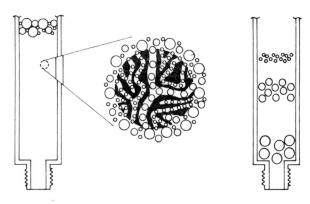

Fig. 3-23. Visualization of the separation process
in size exclusion chromatography. The molecules of
the sample components can only enter those pores
the diameter of which is larger than the cross-
section of the molecules. Thus, the smallest
molecules spend the longest time in the particles
since they can enter all the pores while the
molecules having a cross-section larger than the
diameter of the largest pores will pass by without
entering any pore. Therefore, the large molecules
will elute first off the column while the smallest
molecules will be the last.

The idealized drawing in the middle shows one
particle with pores of different diameters. The
individual molecules are represented by the circles.

diameter of the pores. Thus, the larger molecules
pass quickly through the column while the small
molecules will emerge later because they also
have to diffuse in and out of the pores. Figure
3-23 visualizes the process.

As a result of this process, the chromatogram
obtained shows the larger molecules forming the
early peaks and the smallest molecules, the final
peaks. Since the size of a molecule is related to
its molecular weight, the elution time (or volume)
of a given peak can give a fairly good approximation of its molecular weight. Of course, the
shape (linear, globular, etc.) of the molecule
will also have some effect.

Above, we discussed peaks. Actually, in size-
exclusion chromatography, individual peaks are
relatively rare and are obtained only if discrete
compounds are analyzed, each having a well-defined

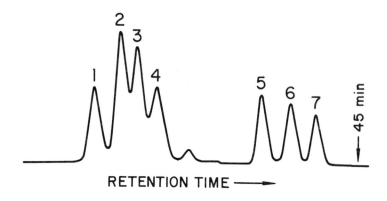

Fig. 3-24. Size-exclusion chromatogram of triglycerides.
Column: two 25 cm x 8 mm ID Shodex A802 + one 25 cm x 8 mm ID Shodex A801.
Mobile phase: tetrahydrofuran, 1 mL/min. RI detector.
Peaks: 1 tristearin (MW=891.5), 2 trimyristin (723.2), 3 trilaurin (639.0), 4 tricaprin (554.9), 5 tributyrin (302.4), 6 tripropionin (260.3), 7 triacetin (218.2).

molecular weight. Such chromatograms are shown in Figures 3-24 and 3-25. In the most widely used applications, the determination of the molecular weight distribution of polymers, the chromatograms consist of one or more composite peaks such as shown in Figure 3-26.

Size-exclusion chromatograms are usually evaluated by determining the molecular weights corresponding to a given retention time (volume), with the help of predetermined calibration curves. For this purpose, standard mixtures representing components with known molecular weights are analyzed. The top part of Figure 3-27 shows such an idealized chromatogram. Subsequently, the retention times (volumes) are plotted against the logarithms of the corresponding molecular weights as shown in the lower part of Figure 3-27. The first peak usually represents molecules of the sample components which would not "fit" any of the pores ("total exclusion"), while the last peak corresponds to the sample components having the smallest molecules which could penetrate all of the available pores ("total permeation"). If even smaller molecules would be present in an

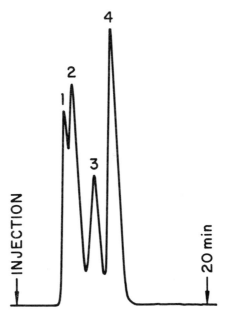

Fig. 3-25. Size-exclusion chromatogram of a
polystyrene standard mixture.
Column: four 25 cm x 2.6 mm ID, each packed with
controlled-porosity glass beads of various pore
sizes. Mobile phase: chloroform, 0.75 mL/min.
UV detector.
Peaks: polystyrenes with molecular weights of 1
2,300,000, 2 451,000, 3 34,500 and 4 3,550.

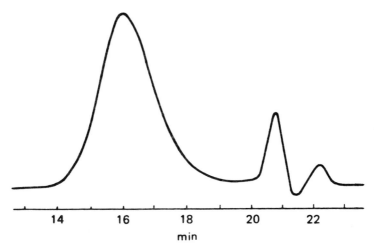

Fig. 3-26. Size-exclusion chromatogram of a
poly(methyl methacrylate) sample.
Column: two 25 cm x 8 mm ID Shodex A80M. Mobile
phase: tetrahydrofuran, 1 mL/min. RI detector.

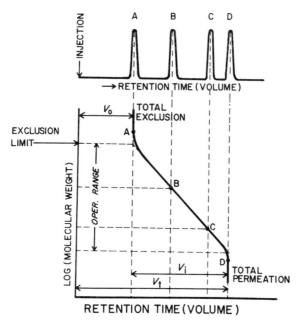

Fig. 3-27. Establishment of a calibration curve for size-exclusion chromatography. A standard sample consisting of polystyrenes with known molecular weights is analyzed (top); subsequently the retention times are plotted against the logarithm of the corresponding molecular weights.

actual sample, they would also penetrate all of the pores and thus, would elute at the same place as peak D.

Now if an actual sample is analyzed, the molecular weights corresponding to certain retention times (volumes) are directly read from this calibration curve.

In size-exclusion chromatography, the classical term of capacity ratio (k) (capacity factor) is misleading. When dealing with it in Part Two, we specified the meaning of V_M, i.e., the mobile phase volume corresponding to t_M, as the void volume of the column. Since

$$k = \frac{t_R - t_M}{t_M} = \frac{V_R - V_M}{V_M} \qquad (12)$$

a nonretarded peak ($t_R = t_M$) will have a capacity
factor of zero and all peaks which are retarded
by the stationary phase will have a capacity
factor higher than zero. In other words, in a
regular chromatogram, the first peak may have a
capacity factor value of k=0 (if it represents a
nonretarded component) and the longer the retention time, the larger the value of the capacity
factor.

The situation is different in size-exclusion
chromatography. Here there is no "retardation"
due to adsorption or partition. The void volume
is equal to the free volume between the particles
plus the volume of the pores; thus, t_M represents
the time the mobile phase molecules (which are
certainly smaller than the pores' diameter), will
pass through all this volume. On the other hand,
sample components - the molecules which are larger
than the diameter of the pores - will pass more
quickly through the column because they are
physically unable to get into these pores. In
other words, using the classical definition for
the capacity factor, the last peak would have a
value of k=0.

The elution volume of the first peak will correspond to the void volume excluding the volumes of
the pores, i.e., the "empty" volume between the
particles and the difference between the elution
volume of the last and first peak gives the total
volume of the pores of the packing in the column.

In order to avoid any confusion, it is convenient
to use the following nomenclature (cf. Figure
3-27):

V_t is the retention (elution) volume of the last
peak representing the total volume of mobile
phase in the column (i.e., the volume between
the particles and the total volume of the
pores);

V_o is the retention volume of the first peak
i.e., the volume of mobile phase within the
column, but outside the particles, i.e., the
interparticle volume;

V_i is the total volume of the mobile phase
       within the packing particles in their pores,
       i.e., the intraparticle volume; $V_i = V_t - V_o$;

k_o the distribution coefficient is a value
       expressing the relative position of a par-
       ticular peak within a chromatogram:

$$k_o = \frac{V_R - V_o}{V_t - V_o} = \frac{V_R - V_o}{V_i} \qquad (13)$$

where V_R is the retention (elution) volume
of the peak.

For the last peak, $V_R - V_t$ and thus, $k_o = 1$
(total permeation) while for the first peak,
$V_R = V_0$ and thus, $k_o = 0$ (total exclusion).

3.62   THE COLUMN PACKING

As mentioned earlier, modern column packing used
in size-exclusion chromatography consists of rigid
polymer gels with controlled pore sizes. For convenience, usually the possible molecular weight
range of the sample which can be analyzed on the
particular packing is specified instead of the
pore diameter. This is determined in a way similar
to the plot on Figure 2-27. For a small volume
sample component, benzene is usually selected
(except with the lowest range materials), the
molecules of which can freely enter all the pores
of the packing.

Table 3-6 lists the operating ranges of the
various Shodex packings* used in size-exclusion
chromatography. They have an uniform particle size
of 10 μm. The standard column length is 25 cm; it
has an I.D. of 8 mm and an O.D. of 10 mm. If
longer columns are needed or if packings of different pore diameter (different operating range)
are to be combined, two or more columns may be
connected in series. In A-80M/S four packings are
already combined in one column.

---

*Shodex packings are manufactured by Showa-Denko
K.K. of Tokyo, Japan.

As indicated in Table 3-6, the usual columns for exclusion chromatography have a wider internal diameter than used in HPLC. If needed, longer columns may also be used.

Table 3-6.   Operating Range of Various Shodex Packings Used in Size Exclusion Chromatography.

MOBILE PHASE	TYPE*	OPERATING RANGE (MOLECULAR WEIGHT)	
ORGANIC LIQUIDS	A801/S	50 -	1,000
	A802/S	50 -	5,000
	A803/S	400 -	70,000
	A804/S	1,000 -	500,000
	A805/S	10,000 -	5,000,000
	A806/S	100,000 -	50,000,000
	A80M/S**	400 -	50,000,000
WATER	S801/S	50 -	1,000
	S802/S	50 -	5,000
	S803/S	300 -	50,000
	S804/S	1,000 -	500,000
	S805/S	10,000 -	5,000,000

*   Prefix A specifies gels used with an organic, and S (for sulfonated) with an aqueous mobile phase. Suffix S specifies the column dimensions: 25 cm long, 10 mm OD and 8 mm ID.

** A80M/S consists of a single 25 cm long column packed with equal portions of A803, A804, A805, and A806 gel. This column can thus be used for broad-range distribution analysis. An A80M/S coupled in series with an A802/S can be used for screening purposes or to obtain a complete range of size distribution analysis.

3.63 THE MOBILE PHASE

The eluting liquid in size-exclusion chromatography should serve only as a carrier for the

sample and should not interact with the sample or
the column packing. Ideally, the sample should be
very soluble in the mobile phase. If the sample
is only sparingly soluble in it, other effects
such as adsorption or partitioning may occur and
a false molecular weight value may be obtained.

One simple test for whether molecular size-
exclusion is the true mechanism in a separation
is to analyze separately a low-molecular weight
substance (typically benzene) on the column
under the same conditions. As discussed earlier,
since the molecules of this substance would be
able to enter all the available pores of the
packing, the elution volume would be equal to V_t
in Figure 3-27. In the chromatogram of the
actual sample, no peak should have an elution
volume larger than this value. Therefore, if
there is any peak with an elution volume larger
than this experimentally determined V_t value,
we may assume that the actual mechanism of separation also involves effects other than size-
exclusion. In such a case, another liquid should
be selected as the mobile phase.

There are many liquids which may be used as the
mobile phase in size-exclusion chromatography.
With the organic-phase column packings, methylene
chloride, chloroform, toluene or tetrahydrofuran
are typical mobile phases. The aqueous-phase
packings are used with water, or occasionally,
alcohols. These liquids cannot be used with the
organic-phase packings because they cause shrink-
ing of the beads.

3.64 APPLICATIONS OF SIZE-EXCLUSION CHROMATOGRAPHY

Two important applications areas are discussed
here separately: size distribution analysis, and
the separation of low molecular weight species.

3.641 SIZE DISTRIBUTION ANALYSIS

The most common use for size-exclusion chromatography is in the quality control of high-molec-
ular weight polymers. These applications demand
an extremely high degree of control over the
properties of the polymer. A knowledge of the

molecular weight distribution of a polymer is the
best way to assure that its physical properties
will be satisfactory: strength, flexibility,
rigidity, brittleness, and tackiness can all be
readily determined from size-distribution analyses.

Polyvinylchloride floor coverings represent a
typical example where size-distribution analysis
is used to control the quality of the original
polymer. These floor coverings must be manufactured to be flexible enough to resist breaking
when rolling and handling, yet be hard enough to
wear well and resist scratching. Figure 3-28
shows the chromatogram obtained when analyzing a
good and a bad batch of material. The bad material
had a 'sticky' feel: obviously, it had a too low
a molecular weight.

As it was already mentioned earlier, the chromatograms of polymers in size-distribution analysis
rarely contain a number of peaks as we have come
to expect in the other modes of chromatography;
rather, we see a broad, composite peak corresponding to the distribution of the various molecular-weight molecules present in the polymer. The
goal of such an investigation is to determine the
molecular-weight distribution of the sample. This

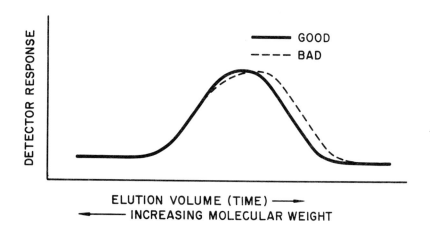

Fig. 3-28. Size exclusion chromatogram of two
vinyl chloride polymers used in the preparation
of floor covering, one good and one insufficient.

is done by dividing the distribution curve - the chromatogram - into fractions or 'slices' as shown in Figure 3-29. Using calibration curves as shown in Figure 3-27, by comparing the retention time (volume) of a particular slice with the curve and reading the corresponding molecular weight, the (average) molecular weight corresponding to each slice can be obtained. From these data, values can be calculated which best describe the actual sample.

At first glance, one would think that the average molecular weight of the sample would represent a meaningful value. This is, however, not so. Figure 3-30 shows the distribution curve of three samples; the average molecular weight of all three samples is the same broken line, but it is obvious that the samples must have quite different characteristics. Sample A has a wider range of larger molecules than the other two, and sample C represents a much wider molecular-weight distribution than sample B. For practical evaluation of the samples, values are needed which describe all these characteristics.

It is beyond the scope of this publication to examine the theoretical basis of these values; for details see the following Perkin-Elmer report:

> Theory of Gel Permeation Chromatography.
> Liquid Chromatography Report No. TN-86.
> (August 1979).

In this book, only the individual terms and their practical meanings are given; each of these represent various moments of the distribution curve and Figure 3-31 indicates their statistical importance. From these, the first two are used most widely:

- The number-average molecular weight (M_N) is the first moment of the curve. It is used to determine flexibility, tackiness, etc., which are related to the proportion of low-molecular weight material.

- The weight-average molecular weight (M_W) is the second moment of the curve. It provides

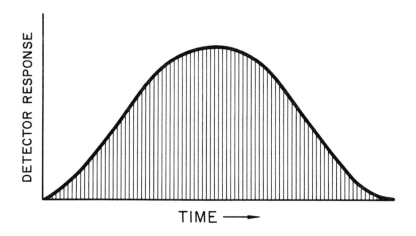

Fig. 3-29. Time-sliced size-exclusion chromatogram, for the evaluation of the sample characteristics.

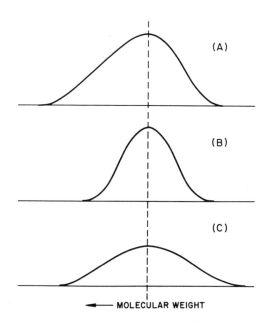

Fig. 3-30. Three distribution curves having the same average molecular weight value.

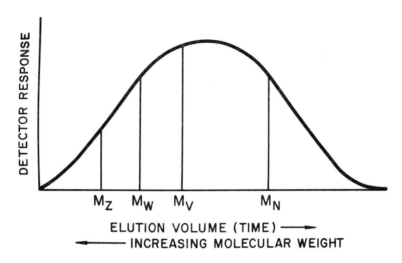

Fig. 3-31. Comparison of the various calculated molecular-weight values.

an accurate evaluation of the proportion of higher weight material which contributes to strength, etc.

- The z-average molecular weight (M_Z) is the third moment of the curve. It is used to monitor the presence of very high molecular weight material in the product, frequently critical in aging and brittleness.

- The viscosity-average molecular weight (M_V) is the fourth moment of the curve. It relates the average viscosity of the material to its molecular weight.

Another important value is the ratio M_W/M_N which expresses the polydispersity or inhomogeneity of the sample. The sharper the distribution curve (i.e., the narrower the distribution range), the smaller this value. For homogeneous polymers, its value would be 1.0; for polymers with very narrow molecular weight distribution values of 1.05 to 1.2 may be obtained while for technical polymers the quotient may have a value as high as 10.

As an illustration, Table 3-7 lists values for the two distribution curves in Figure 3-28.

Table 3-7. Characteristic Values Corresponding
to the Distribution Curves Shown in Figure 3-28.

		GOOD PVC	BAD PVC
M_W	Weight-average molecular weight	106,000	103,000
M_N	Number-average molecular weight	29,000	22,000
M_W/M_N	Polydispersity	3.66	4.68

The calculations required to achieve the distribution analyses are laborious and time-consuming,
thus the recent availability of "GPC Calculation
Programs" for laboratory computers, such as
Perkin-Elmer's SIGMA 10 Chromatography Data
Station, has proven to be a valuable asset to the
polymer chemist. The high degree of flexibility
and precision provided by this program is described
in the following Perkin-Elmer report:

The Perkin-Elmer Gel Permeation System.
Liquid Chromatography Report No. TN-87.
(August 1979).

3.642 SEPARATION OF LOW-MOLECULAR-WEIGHT SPECIES

Exclusion chromatography can be used for separating compounds even if one does not wish to determine the molecular weights. In fact, this technique
is used to pretreat or prescreen complex mixtures
with fractions of each molecular-weight range
collected for rechromatographing on more specific
separating columns.

Discrete separations of species are capable of
being obtained when the higher resolving rigid
divinylbenzene gels (Shodex) are used, especially
when the more compact molecules having molecular
weights below 2000 are being examined. Figures
3-32 and 3-33 illustrate this. In the first case,
the same column can resolve higher molecular-

weight polymers and phthalate esters where the
molecular-weight difference in one case is less
than 30; in the second case, compounds with molecular-weight difference of only 14 are resolved.

Figure 3-32 also illustrates how increasing the
column length can improve separation. A similar
effect could be achieved by reducing the mobile
phase flow rate.

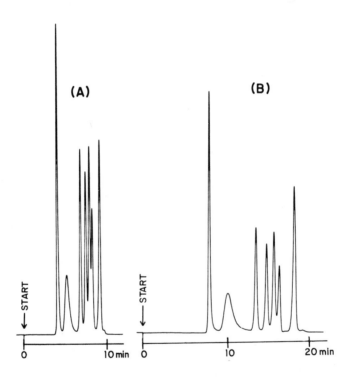

*Fig. 3-32. Separation of low molecular-weight
compounds by size-exclusion chromatography.
Column: Shodex A802, 8 mm ID; length: A 25 cm
column, B two 25 cm columns in series.
Mobile phase: tetrahydrofuran, 1 mL/min. UV
detector at 260 nm.
Peaks: 1 polystyrene (MW=20,400), 2 polystyrene
(2,100), 3 dioctyl phthalate (390.6), 4 dibutyl
phthalate (278.3), 5 diethyl phthalate (222.2),
6 dimethyl phthalate (194.2), 7 benzene (78.12).*

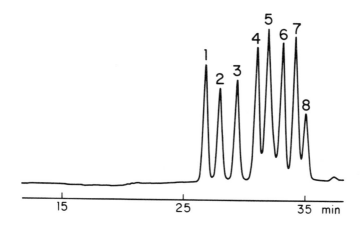

Fig. 3-33. Separation of alkylbenzenes by
exclusion chromatography.
Column: four 25 cm x 8 mm ID Shodex A801 in
series.
Mobile phase: tetrahydrofuran. Flow rate: 1 mL/min.
Peaks: 1 n-decylbenzene (MW=218.4), 2 n-octylbenzene
(190.3), 3 n-hexylbenzene (162.3), 4 n-butylbenzene
(134.2), 5 n-propylbenzene (120.2), 6 ethylbenzene
(106.2), 7 toluene (92.1), 8 benzene (78.12).

3.7 ION-EXCHANGE CHROMATOGRAPHY

3.71 PRINCIPLES

Ionic compounds are often best separated and
analyzed by ion-exchange chromatography with the
help of ion-exchangers as the stationary phase.
These consist of materials which carry surplus
positive or negative electric charges. The charge
is balanced by an eluting stream containing a
stoichiometric equivalent of ions of the opposite
polarity. These are the counterions which can be
exchanged for somewhat similarly charged sample
molecules which are introduced into the stream.
Conservation of neutrality requires that the
amount of counterions displaced by sample ions
must be stoichiometrically equivalent. Therefore,
a strongly charged sample in a weakly charged
eluent will adhere to the column and conversely,
a weakly charged sample molecule will not be able
to displace strong eluent ions, thus will not be
retained in a highly ionized system.

3.72   STATIONARY PHASES

Depending on their function, ion-exchange packings
are either cation exchangers or anion exchangers.
The packings used in liquid chromatography usually
consist of high molecular-weight polymers or
silica gel to which ionic groups are chemically
bonded. The particular advantage of silica-based
materials is mechanical strength; due to this,
they resist compression or expansion with pressure
changes and do not swell or contract with changes
in pH and ionic strength as do the polymer gel-type
materials. A further advantage of the silica-based
materials is that they can be used with organic or
water/organic mobile phases. (Table 3-8).

The cation exchangers contain either sulfonic acid
(strong cationic) or carboxylic acid (weak
cationic) groups while the anion exchangers have
quaternary ammonium groups bonded through some
intermediate groups to the silicon atoms. Figure
3-34 shows the structure of the characteristic
surface groups as well as illustrating the ion-
exchange mechanism.

3.73   THE MOBILE PHASE

There are three mobile-phase variables which affect
the retention of an ionic solute on an ion-exchange

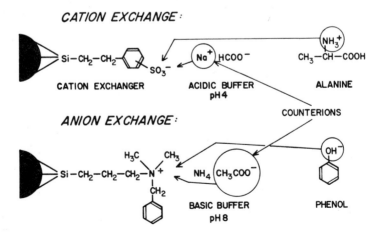

Fig. 3-34. Structure of characteristic ion-exchange
packings and the ion-exchange mechanism.

Table 3-8. Typical Silica-bonded Ion-exchange Packings.

TRADE NAME	CHARACTERISTICS	ACTIVE GROUP	TYPE	PARTICLE SIZE	TYPICAL ION EXCHANGE CAPACITY meq/g	pH RANGE
ION-X-SC	strong cation exchangers	$-SO_3^{2-}$	Pellicular	37-42	0.01-0.1	2-7.5
Partisil 10 SCX			Fully porous	10	0.5-2	2-9
ION-X-SA	strong anion exchangers	quaternary ammonium	Pellicular	37-42	0.01-0.1	2-7.5
Partisil 10 SAX			Fully porous	10	0.5-2	2-9

column: ionic strength, pH adjustment, and organic
modifier. The most important of these is the adjustment of the ionic strength. This is done with
the help of buffer salts.

3.731 MODIFICATION OF THE IONIC STRENGTH

The ionic strength is related to the concentration
and charge of the dissolved ions in the eluent.
Control of the ionic strength is critical, since
this strength is simply a measure of the number
of counterions in the mobile phase. The number of
counterions must be controlled since this is what
established the delicate equilibrium on the active
sites of the ion exchanger and allows the sample
to be alternately attracted and displaced as it
moves through the column. If the counterion concentration in the mobile phase is too high, sample
ions will not find any available sites and will
not be retarded. Conversely, if the counterion
concentration is too low, the sample ions will not
be eluted from the column.

Complex samples may contain components having
charges varying from weak to strong. Complete
elution of this type of sample frequently requires
a gradient elution pattern, where elution begins
with a mobile phase of low molarity (often simply
pH-adjusted deionized water) and a component with
higher molarity is gradually introduced into the
system, providing sufficient ionic strength to
displace the most strongly attracted sample ions
from the exchanger.

Table 3-9 lists some of the most frequently used
ionic modifiers (buffer salts), together with their
useful pH ranges. From these, probably the
phosphate buffers, sodium acetate, and sodium borate
are used most frequently. Note that chloride salts
are not included in the Table; these attack the
Type 316 stainless steel of which most of the
instruments are constructed and therefore, are not
recommended.

Some ions are much more effective than others in
reducing retention time. Specifically: in cation
exchange separations, potassium ions are more

Table 3-9. Buffer Salts Widely Used in Ion-Exchange Chromatography.

BUFFER SALT*	USEFUL pH RANGE
Citric acid	2.0 - 6.0
Ammonium *phosphate*	2.2 - 6.5
Potassium hydrogen *phthalate***	2.2 - 6.5
Disodium hydrogen *citrate*	2.6 - 6.5
Sodium *formate*	3.0 - 4.4
Sodium *acetate*	4.2 - 5.4
Triethanolamine	6.7 - 8.7
Sodium *borate*	8.0 - 9.8
Sodium *perchlorate*	8.0 - 9.8
Sodium *nitrate*	8.0 - 10.0
Ammonium *acetate*	8.6 - 9.8
Sodium dihydrogen *phosphate*	2.0-6.0 and 8.0-12.0
Potassium dihydrogen *phosphate*	2.0-8.0 and 9.0-13.0

*   The italicized moity is the active (exchanged) ion.

** Phthalate has a high UV cutoff and therefore, should not be used with UV detectors.

effective than sodium ions in reducing retention and in anionic exchange, perchlorate and nitrate are more powerful than phosphate. Thus, when the sample species has relatively weak charges (e.g., vitamins, nucleic acids, phenothiazines) the most easily controlled system will be that using the buffers of lower strength. When strongly charged species such as carboxylic acids, organic amines, etc., are to be separated, the stronger buffers should be used.

3.732 ADJUSTMENT OF THE pH VALUE

The second variable affecting the retention of an ionic solute is the pH, particularly in the case of weak anionic and cationic exchanges. For example, a decrease in the pH - that is, an increase in the hydrogen-ion concentration - will reduce the ionization of weak cation-exchangers. Similarly, increase in the pH can decrease the ionization of weak anion-exchangers. On the other hand, with strong anionic or cationic exchangers or when highly ionized samples are analyzed, changes in the pH will have little or no effect on the retention times of the sample components.

In cases where the pH does affect the separation, the proper range can be selected by considering the pKa, the logarithm of the Ka value. The Ka is expressed in the Bronstead acid-base concept as a primary measure of the thermodynamic equilibrium acidity constant of a material, or more simply, as a means of describing the extent of ionic activity of materials. The stronger the acid, the greater the value of Ka. Since Ka values may vary over orders of magnitude, it is more convenient to use the pKa values:

$$pKa = -\log_{10} Ka \qquad (14)$$

Thus, the stronger the acid, the smaller the pKa, and conversely, the smaller the pKa of the conjugate acid (BH+), the weaker the base (B). To correlate the pKa with pH, the Henderson-Hassel-Balch equation states:

$$pH = pKa \pm \log \frac{\text{ionized}}{\text{un-ionized}} \qquad (15)$$

When the mobile phase pH has a strong effect on the ionic nature of weakly acidic or basic sample molecules, if the pH of the buffer in the mobile phase is adjusted to be equal to the pKa of the weakly acidic or basic sample, that sample will only be 50% in the ionic form. Since only the ionic form of the sample is retarded or bound to the ionic exchange packing, a small change in the pH can greatly affect the proportion of sample which is ionized and thus affect its retention time.

As a general rule of thumb, the pH of the buffer selected should be one-to-two pH units below the pKa of bases and one-to-two pH units above the pKa of acids:

$$pH \text{ (bases)} = pKa - 1.5 \qquad (16)$$

$$pH \text{ (acids)} = pKa + 1.5 \qquad (17)$$

If the pKa is not known, it can be approximated in many cases. For example, most simple primary, secondary, and tertiary aliphatic amines have pKa values between 9.5 and 11.0, while those of aromatic amines are between 5 and 7. The pKa value of carboxylic acids is around 5 and of phenols around 10. Strong acids (HCl, HNO_3, etc.) have negative values while the pKa values of strong bases (KOH, NaOH, etc.) are above 15. Naturally, in the last two cases, the general rule would not apply anymore, but samples so reactive are not commonly investigated by chromatography.

A final caution in regard to pH adjustment involves the concept of the isoelectric point. Since this is the point, or pH, at which the net charge on the molecule in solution is zero, with the positive and negative groups within the molecule equally ionized, the molecule has no charge and therefore, cannot be retained on an ion-exchange column unless the pH is changed.

3.733 THE POSSIBLE USE OF ORGANIC SOLVENTS AS MOBILE PHASE COMPONENTS

Since many of the sample species separated by ion exchange are water soluble and almost all of the buffer salts are insoluble in organics, most mobile phase systems are primarily aqueous. As more efficient packing materials become available, it is becoming common to be able to separate extremely complex mixtures which often contain ionizable compounds that are insoluble in water. These materials may then be adsorbed onto the column so strongly that they cannot be eluted. Since they are held by adsorptive forces, ionic modification cannot displace them, and a water-miscible organic modifier must be added to the aqueous mobile phase to displace the sample from the column. Ordinarily, an excess (30 to 50%) of organic modifier is used to assure that no adsorption activity will inter-

fere with the desired ion exchange process, but
occasionally, the organic constituent may be opti-
mized as in the adsorption or reversed-phase mode,
to achieve retention and resolution of some sample
components.

3.8 ION-PAIR CHROMATOGRAPHY

3.81 PRINCIPLES

Sometimes known as ion-pair extraction or ion-pair
partition chromatography, or as "soap" chromatography, ion-pairing adds a new dimension of analytical capability to HPLC. Use of this technique
allows the separation of many materials which are
too highly ionized to be separated by normal
adsorption or partition methods, but too insoluble
in water to be analyzed by conventional ion-
exchange techniques. However, once mastered, the
technique is so convenient that it may be preferentially used even if strong ionic compounds are
water soluble. Since it brackets a wide range of
parameters, ion-pairing can be used to separate
samples which contain strong ionic, weak ionic
and nonionic species, as well as those which
contain both acids and bases.

Ion-pairing is currently being performed most
successfully on permanently bonded reversed-phase
columns. Generally, these columns are the most
effective for the separation of nonionic compounds
since the primary separations mechanism involves
selective solubility, hence partitioning between
a hydrophilic mobile phase and a lipophilic
stationary phase. The presence of ionic moities in
these systems generally interferes with this solubility. In the case of weak acids and bases having
pKa values between 2 and 8, the ionic activity can
be suppressed by buffering the mobile phase to
suppress this ionization. Strong acids and bases,
which have pH values outside of this range, cannot be readily suppressed. The purpose of ion-
pairing is to add a second ion to the eluent which
will combine with the sample ions, effectively
binding them up creating a neutral ion-pair which
then will undergo the normal partitioning or other
distribution process between the stationary and

mobile phases. From this point on, changes in retention time are accomplished by using standard reversed-phase techniques such as adjusting the organic/inorganic solvent ratio.

Ion-pairing may also be used to modify the sample ions and have the newly formed, paired-ion participate in the ion-exchange process. Finally, the third variant of the technique is to use ion-pair chromatography to modify the stationary phase. In this case, the counterion adsorbs on the column packing and now, the oppositely charged sample ions will bond to this new, counterion surface. The excess counterions in the mobile phase are needed to maintain a constant counterion concentration on the stationary phase surface and contribute to the distribution process.

In all these variants, the parameters which can be varied to obtain a wide range of selectivity are: the type and concentration of the counterion, the pH, the column temperature, and the type and composition of the mobile phase.

3.82 COLUMN SELECTION

As mentioned, the column most commonly used in ion-pairing is the C-18 (ODS) reversed-phase type. The same column used for normal (nonionic) reversed-phase work may be used intermittently in both modes: however, it is recommended whenever possible to dedicate a column for permanent use by ion-pair chromatography, using a different column for the other type work. The reason for this is that frequent use of ion-pairing reagents will lead to permanent changes in the column's activity when used in normal reversed-phase work.

Generally, a narrow-bore column packed with totally porous, small (5-15 μm) particles with a bonded phase is recommended. Some researchers prefer standard microparticulate silica columns coated in situ with the stationary phase thus performing classical partition chromatography but, naturally, now including a counterion in the mobile phase to achieve ion-pairing. While this sometimes provides a higher degree of selectivity for specific compounds, it bears the disadvantages noted in the

use of nonbonded columns in the partition mode of
HPLC, such as column bleed and detector interference.

3.83 COUNTERION SELECTION

In order to assure that all weakly ionizable materials are suppressed and all strong ions completely
ionized, counterions having very high or very low
pKa values are used. The selection of counterions
depends on the sample.

Basic samples are commonly analyzed using the
sodium salt of alkylsulfonates such as e.g.,
sodium 1-heptanesulfonate, with the pH adjusted
to about 3 with glacial acetic acid. Less frequently used counterions are sodium lauryl
sulfonate and sodium dioctylsulfocyanate. Essentially, the analysis is performed at low pH values
(2.5 to 3.5).

Acidic samples are commonly analyzed with tetra-
butyl ammonium phosphate which provides a pH of
about 7.5; other possibilities are tributylamine
or tridecylamine; the pH range is 7-8.

In both cases, a counterion concentration between
0.003 and 0.005 molar is sufficient to achieve
full ionization of most sample species without
introducing harmful side effects such as detector
saturation or crystal formation and subsequent
system blockage.

Note that is is generally not advisable to allow
the counterion-containing mobile phase to remain
on the column or in the instrument when there is
no flow: the instrument and the column should be
rinsed with distilled water or the mixture of
water and organic solvent used as the mobile
phase. It is also recommended that silica-based
columns (particularly ODS columns) are never used
at a pH over 7.5 - 8.0.

3.9 DEVELOPING A CHROMATOGRAPHIC METHOD

Liquid chromatography methods development has for
many consisted of laboriously trying solvent after
solvent with a range of LC columns. In the early

stages of learning how to obtain quality chromatograms, this trial-and-error process can be frus-
trating. This waste of time and solvent is many
times unnecessary. However, for the new chromatographer, the decisions as to which steps should
come first for efficient LC methods development,
is not always clear.

This part of our book describes a systematic out-
line for the chromatographer to follow in developing a LC method. By using the procedures described here, it should be possible to significantly reduce the amount of time required in
optimizing LC methods.

This part is based on the following report published by the Liquid Chromatography Product Depart-
ment of Perkin-Elmer:

> W.E. Shumaker: LC Methods Development
> Procedure - A Description. LC Brochure
> No. TN-69. (June 1978).

3.91 SELECTION OF LIQUIDS TO BE USED AS THE MOBILE PHASE

Before anything else can be done, it is necessary
to select the possible solvents to be used as the
mobile phase. In contrast to gas chromatography
which uses one single gas as the mobile phase,
many separations in liquid chromatography require
the use of two or more mobile phase components;
also, the chromatographic mode selected and the
available detectors have certain requirements to
be followed in the selection of the liquid(s)
which may be used to form the mobile phase. Some
of these requirements might be contradictory;
therefore, it is not enough to start with only
one or two possibilities: we should expect to
initially encounter a number of variables which
must be controlled, then reduce them according
to the requirements of the specific separation
problem.

Table 3-3 has already listed a large number of
liquids used in the practice of LC as mobile phase

components. That table included a number of numerical data to be used when considering the selection of the proper liquids. Table 3-10 supplements this list by characterizing each liquid in relation to its application. A few physical constants are also included in Table 3-10; these values have no direct relationship to the chromatographic separation process, but knowledge of them is sometimes useful: e.g., the boiling point helps in selecting the proper conditions for storage, etc.

3.911 SAMPLE SOLUBILITY AND STABILITY

It is obvious that a liquid in which the sample to be analyzed is totally insoluble, cannot be used as the mobile phase. Thus, our systematic selection procedure must start by the determination of the solubility of the sample in several of the commonly used solvents. This can be done in the following ways: a few milligrams of the sample placed in several vials, each filled with a different chromatographic solvent, provides a rapid visualization of solubility.

This evaluation of solubilities is essential to avoid a mobile phase which will precipitate all or part of the sample in the instrument. Typical chromatographic solvents used for this test might include hexane, toluene, chloroform, tetrahydrofuran, acetonitrile, methanol and water.

The evaluation is not complete without also checking how stable the sample is in the chromatographic solvent. It is much less costly to observe possible instability of these initial solutions in a sample vial than to learn of the problem later through ruined columns or unstable chromatography.

3.912 SAMPLE SIZE

Before we go further, we must consider our basic goal: are we doing liquid chromatography for analytical or for preparative purposes? If the goal is preparative chromatography, with the corresponding higher sample sizes, this would automatically restrict our choice of the chroma-

Table 3-10. Characteristics of Organic Liquids Used as Mobile Phase Components in Liquid Chromatography.*

LIQUID	MW	DENSITY	BOILING POINT °C	REMARKS
Acetic acid	60.05	1.049	117.9	Useful acidic additive.
Acetone	58.08	0.818	56.5	Not UV but good solvent and cheap.
Acetonitrile	41.06	0.782	82.0	Expensive but otherwise ideal.
Aniline	93.13	1.022	184.4	
Benzene	78.12	0.879	80.1	Not UV.
Bromoethane (ethyl bromide)	108.97	1.460	38.35	Expensive.
Carbon disulfide	76.14	1.260	46.2	Smelly, toxic and flammable; not UV.
Carbon tetrachloride	153.80	1.590	76.8	Rather viscous; poor UV.
Chlorobenzene	112.56	1.106	131.7	Not UV.
1-Chlorobutane	92.57	0.873	68.3	Expensive.
Chloroform	119.39	1.500	61.2	UV not ideal.
2-Chloropropane	78.54	0.862	35.74	Expensive.
Cyclohexane	84.16	0.779	81.4	More viscous but selectivity different from hexane.
Cyclopentane	70.14	0.740	49.3	Expensive.
Decahydronaphthalene	138.25	0.896	194.6	Used hot (typically 130°C.)
1,2-Dichlorobenzene (ODCB)	147.00	1.306	180.48	Best chlorinated solvent for UV.
1,2-Dichloroethane	96.95	1.250	83.0	Limited UV; basic.
Diethylamine	73.12	0.702	55.5	
Diethyl ether	74.12	0.713	34.6	Peroxide hazard; BP too low.
Dimethoxyethane	90.12	0.863	83.0	

LIQUID	MW	DENSITY	BOILING POINT °C	REMARKS
Dimethyl acetamide	87.12	0.937	165.0	Exclusion chromatography.
N,N-Dimethylformamide	73.10	0.949	153.0	Viscous, except as a minor component.
Dimethyl sulfoxide	78.13	1.100	189.0	Purification needed to achieve good UV.
Dioxane	88.11	1.033	101.3	
Di-n-propyl ether	102.20	0.747	89.64	Peroxide hazard, low boiling.
1,2-Ethanediol	62.07	1.114	197.3	Too viscous.
Ethanol	46.07	0.789	78.5	More viscous than methanol but more miscible.
Ethyl acetate	88.10	0.901	77.15	UV not ideal.
Ethyl sulfide	90.19	0.836	92.1	Not UV.
Fluoroalkanes	290-340	$\approx$ 1.7	$\approx$57.0	
n-Hexane	86.17	0.659	69.0	Good UV.
Methanol	32.04	0.796	64.7	Cheap and excellent if pure enough.
2-Methoxyethanol	76.10	0.965	124.6	Good UV if pure enough.
Methylene chloride	84.94	1.336	40.1	UV not ideal.
Methyl acetate	74.08	0.927	57.1	UV not ideal.
Methyl ethyl ketone	72.11	0.805	79.6	Not UV.
Methylnaphthalene	142.19	1.025	235.0	Exclusion chromatography.
N-methylpyrrolidone	85.15	0.819	202.0	Exclusion chromatography at high temp. (165°C); less corrosive than OBCB.
Nitromethane	61.04	1.138	101.2	Expensive, not UV.
1-Nitropropane	89.10	1.001	131.2	Not UV.

LIQUID	MW	DENSITY	BOILING POINT °C	REMARKS
n-Pentane	72.15	0.629	36.2	Low BP; more expensive but less toxic than hexane.
1-Pentanol	88.15	0.815	137.8	Not readily available.
1-Pentene	70.14	0.640	30.0	More viscous than ethanol and
2-Propanol	60.10	0.786	82.3	methanol; a popular additive.
Pyridine	79.10	0.983	115.3	Limited UV; basic.
Tetrachloroethylene	165.80	1.620	121.0	Exclusion chromatography.
Tetrahydrofuran	72.10	0.880	66.0	Peroxide problems.
Toluene	92.15	0.867	110.6	Not UV.
1,1,2-Trichloroethylene	131.40	1.460	87.2	Exclusion chromatography.
1,1,2-Trichlorotri-fluoroethane	187.40	1.563	47.6	
Triethylamine	101.10	0.728	89.5	Basic.
Trifluoroethanol	100.04	1.390	73.6	Exclusion chromatography.
2,2,4-Trimethyl-pentane (isooctane)	114.20	0.692	99.3	Higher BP and more viscous than benzene.
Water	18.02	1.000	100.0	
m-Xylene	106.17	0.864	139.1	Not UV.

* Data taken from the table published in P.A. Bristow: LC in Practice, hetp, Inc., Wilmslow, 1976.

tographic mode to be selected. This is mainly due
to solvent capacity.

The liquids most frequently used with reversed-
phase chromatography are tetrahydrofuran, acetonitrile or methanol mixed with water. Often these
solvents are easily overloaded and analysis is
usually performed at the borderline of compound
solubility in the mobile phase. Thus, reversed-
phase chromatography is generally avoided for
preparative work and the preferred mode is adsorption chromatography with silica as the stationary
phase and hydrocarbon or halocarbon type liquids
as the mobile phase.

There is one more reason why such liquids are preferred in preparative work. There, the goal is to
obtain pure substances by collecting the respective fractions and distilling off the solvent. For
this reason, one prefers liquids with relatively
low boiling points and many hydrocarbons or halo-
carbons fulfill this requirement.

3.913 MODE OF SEPARATION

The next step in mobile phase selection is related
to the choice of the preferred mode of separation.
For example, if the preparation of pure sample
components is desired then, as mentioned above,
one would prefer normal phase adsorption chromatography and thus, select the mobile phase according
to the requirements discussed there. In other
cases, one may have the desire to elute the more
polar peaks first as e.g., in the case of metabol-
ism studies. This would create a preference for
reversed-phase separations. If gradient elution
is preferred, then two miscible solvents are to be
selected; one being a relatively strong, while the
other a weaker, solvent.

One may approach the selection of the mode of
operation and the corresponding stationary and
mobile phases systematically, starting with the
investigation of the sample's characteristics.
Table 3-11 represents an approach to this. Naturally, such a simplified compilation can never be
applied for special cases (and the same is true of
Table 3-12 and 3-13). Still, this table represents

Table 3-11. Systematic Selection of the Variables of Liquid Chromatography.

SOLUBILITY	SAMPLE POLARITY or ACIDITY		MODE OF CHROMATOGRAPHIC ANALYSIS	STATIONARY PHASE	MOBILE PHASE
not water soluble	non-polar		partition (bonded-phase) chromatography; reversed-phase chromatography	C_{18} bonded phase	methanol, or water/acetonitrile (70:30)
	moderately polar		reversed-phase chromatography	C_8 bonded phase	water/acetonitrile (50:50)
	polar		adsorption chromatography; normal-phase chromatography	nondeactivated silica / deactivated silica	n-heptane/chloroform (95:5)
		partition (bonded-phase) chromatography	reversed-phase chromatography	C_8 bonded phase	water/acetonitrile (70:30)
			normal-phase chromatography	CN bonded phase	n-heptane/isopropanol (98:2)
water soluble	basic	strong	ion-exchange chromatography	Cation exchanger	0.01-$0.1M$ Na_2HPO_4
		weak	partition (bonded phase) chromatography; reversed-phase chromatography	C_{18} bonded phase	water (containing 0.005M hexanesulfonic acid)/methanol
	acidic	strong	ion-exchange chromatography	Anion exchanger	0.01-$0.1M$ NaH_2PO_4
		weak	partition (bonded-phase) chromatography; reversed-phase chromatography	C_{18} bonded phase	water/methanol (containing 0.005M tetrabutyl ammonium hydroxide)

a good indication of the approach to be followed when developing a method for liquid chromatography.

Separation of ionic or polar materials from relatively neutral compounds could be best performed by ion exchange. Obviously, for this type of separation, the major component of the mobile phase will be water. Other separation modes utilizing the ionic character of the sample are ion pairing or ion suppression and these also utilize aqueous mobile phases containing the appropriate modifier. Table 3-12 lists typical mobile phases for these modes.

It should be mentioned that the pH of the mobile phase used with bonded phase packings or silica must not be lower than 2 or higher than 7.5. Such mobile phases can destroy the bondings to the silica surface or even dissolve the silica itself.

Separations of materials of significantly different molecular size (usually 10% or more), might be most easily performed by size separation, using exclusion chromatography. An example of this would be the separation of a polymer material from its additives. Naturally, the investigation of the molecular-weight distribution of a polymer is also carried out by this mode. In size-exclusion chromatography, the preferable mobile phases are tetrahydrofuran, chloroform or methylene chloride for substances insoluble in water, and water for those which are soluble in it. Table 3-13 indicates the Shodex-type column packings to be selected according to sample solubility and molecular weight range.

3.914 DETECTION REQUIREMENTS

Detector considerations such as solvent cutoff wavelength in comparison to the compounds' maximum absorption wavelength could also affect the selection of the mobile phase. If the solvent originally planned to be used is masking compound absorbance, a different solvent may be required.

The need to separate a wide range of compound types, i.e., performing separations by gradient elution, can also influence solvent selection.

Table 3-12.   Mobile Phase Selection for the Analysis of Ionized Compounds.

MODE	STRONGLY ACIDIC SAMPLE	SLIGHTLY ACIDIC SAMPLE	SLIGHTLY BASIC SAMPLE	STRONGLY BASIC SAMPLE
ION SUPPRESSION		Example for mobile phase: water/methanol or water/acetonitrile, modified with 0.01-0.1M phosphoric or acetic acid added to the water. To elute sample components vary concentration of organic component.	Example for mobile phase: water/methanol or water/acetonitrile, modified with 0.1M R_2NH or NH_4OH added to the water. To elute sample components vary concentration of organic component.	
ION EXCHANGE	Use a buffer solution as the mobile phase. Example: 0.01M NaH_2PO_4. To elute sample components vary pH or ionic strength of the buffer.		Use a buffer solution as the mobile phase. Example: 0.01M Na_2HPO_4. To elute sample components vary pH or ionic strength of the buffer.	
ION PAIRING	Example for mobile phase: water/methanol modified with 0.005M tetrabutyl ammonium hydroxide (added to the methanol) and appropriate buffer (added to the water). To elute sample components vary methanol concentration.		Example for mobile phase: water/methanol modified with 0.005M hexane sulfonic acid (added to the water). To elute sample components vary methanol concentration.	

Table 3-13.   Column Packings Recommended for Size
Exclusion Chromatography.

SAMPLE SOLUBILITY	SAMPLE MOLECULAR WEIGHT	SHODEX-TYPE TO BE USED AS COLUMN PACKING	MOBILE PHASE
Soluble in water and alcohols	less than 1000	S801	water
	less than 5000	S802	
	over 5000	S803 - S805*	
Insoluble in water and alcohols	less than 1000	A801	Tetrahydrofuran, chloroform, toluene, methylene chloride
	less than 5000	A802	
	over 5000	A80M or A803 - A806*	

*Depending on the actual molecular weight range; for
 individual specifications see Table 3-6.

For example, monitoring at 254 nm with an UV
detector using chloroform during gradient elution
is not recommended because this will result in a
changing baseline corresponding to % chloroform.
Tetrahydrofuran or ethylene dichloride might be a
better choice. Gradient separations using the far
UV for detection will dictate use of solvent pairs
such as hexane/isopropanol or acetonitrile/water
for maximum baseline stability.

If refractive index detectors are used then,
naturally, one must check the refractive index of
the solvents as compared to the sample components
because the greater the difference, the higher
the sensitivity.

3.915 PURITY

In liquid chromatography, it is very important
that both the sample solution and the solvents
used in the mobile phase be pure liquids, free of
any solid particles. Therefore, the sample solution should be filtered before injection into the
chromatograph. Similarly, the solvents used as
the mobile phase should also be filtered through
the same type of filter as was used for the sample.
It is strongly recommended that all sample solutions and liquids (mobile phases) be filtered
below 0.5 μm. The top reducing union in Perkin-
Elmer instruments contains an integral 2 micro-
meter frit which will protect the column from
larger material; however, there is strong evidence
to suggest that small particles, less than 2
micrometers, can cause column failure.

All-glass filtration systems are available for the
filtration of solvents. These systems employ fine
porosity (0.45 μm) cellulose or PTFE filters for
the filtration of aqueous or organic liquids,
respectively. A vacuum pump or aspirator is
normally required to force liquids through these
devices. In addition, sample filtration kits are
available to allow rapid filtration of samples.
These systems utilize filter cartridge-holding
devices which attach to Luer-lok® -equipped
syringes. Both sample and solvent filtration kits
are available from Perkin-Elmer.

Currently, many suppliers of HPLC-grade solvents
include filtration through 0.45 μm filters as one
of their production requirements. It is generally
safe to use these without refiltering if they are
protected during preparation or use.

3.92 STATIONARY PHASE SELECTION

The selection of the stationary phase is a very
complex question and depends on a number of
factors such as the characteristics and complexity
of the sample and the selected mode of separation.
Tables 3-11 through 3-13 gave some recommendations
for general sample types. Naturally, it is
impossible to cover all the possible stationary

phases in such a simplified treatment and these tables serve only as a general guide.

When the chromatographer faces a new separation problem, it is always very important to search the literature to ascertain whether the same type of sample has been analyzed before and if it was, under what conditions and on what kind of column packing. At this point, even if direct copying of the analytical parameters published in the literature might not provide adequate results - after all, samples are usually not exactly alike - they provide a good starting point for further adjustments.

3.93   SELECTION OF COLUMN DIMENSIONS

The variable column dimensions are diameter and length.

3.931   COLUMN DIAMETER

As already mentioned earlier, when speaking about columns and column packings, most HPLC columns available today have an internal diameter of either 2-2.6 or 4.6-5 mm. Decisions on which to use depend on the answers to a number of questions:

is the problem trace analysis, or are we considering a sample with higher component concentration?

is the purpose of the separation to collect fractions or to obtain a record of separations for qualitative and/or quantitative purposes?

is the cost of the solvents used as the mobile phase a question to be considered?

The actual column diameter selection will depend on the concentration of a component in the column effluent, and the volume of mobile phase to be consumed for an analysis. These can be related to the flow rate, or more correctly, the velocity of the mobile phase.

As discussed earlier in connection with the theory of chromatography, the chromatographic process is

a function of the linear velocity of the mobile
phase i.e., the speed at which it passes through
the column. Various chromatographic parameters,
including column efficiency, column pressure,
retention time, and resolution, are a function of
this linear velocity. The linear velocity of the
mobile phase is, itself, a function of both the
volumetric flow (mL/min) of the mobile phase
and the cross-sectional diameter of the column.
Thus, if for a linear velocity of 1 mm/sec, a
2.6 mm I.D. column requires a flow rate of 0.64
mL/min, then a 4.6 mm I.D. column requires a flow
rate of 1.99 mL/min, over three times faster.
Therefore, for the same analysis time and operating pressure, a 4.6 mm I.D. column will use
three times the volume of solvent that is required
by a 2.6 mm I.D. column. If solvent cost is a
consideration, then the 2.6 mm I.D. column is to
be preferred.

Similarly, the volume of mobile phase in which a
component is eluted* (that is, that volume of
solvent containing the component or peak) will be
three times greater for the 4.6 mm I.D. column,
compared to the 2.6 mm I.D. column. If high sensitivity is an important consideration, such as in
trace analysis, then the components should elute
in the smallest volume of solvent possible. For
this reason, the 2.6 mm I.D. column would again
be preferred.

On the other hand, if fraction collection is
needed, e.g., for analysis by other analytical
techniques, then the largest possible sample
weight is desired. The sample-loading capacity is
a function of the amount of packing material present in the column: e.g., a 4.6 mm I.D. column
contains more than three times the packing present
in a 2.6 mm column. For this reason, one prefers
the larger diameter column in such a case.

---

*The meaning of this volume and its calculation
was explained in the footnote in chapter 3.12.

3.932 COLUMN LENGTH

We have already mentioned that in practical liquid
chromatography, the standard column length is 25 cm
and that if a longer column is required, one
prefers to connect two or more such columns in
series rather than to prepare a single column of
comparable length. As mentioned, in liquid chromatography column connection can be accomplished
without significant band-spreading , if done
correctly. Naturally, it is important to select
the proper connectors and Appendix I to this book
gives instructions on the optimum way various
columns should be connected.

3.933 COLUMN HANDLING

Although not directly related to the development
of a LC method, the proper method of handling the
separation columns is an important question to be
considered by every chromatography laboratory. For
this reason, a few recommendations are included
here.

Most columns are shipped with end caps at both
ends of the column. These end caps consist of a
nut and PTFE (teflon) seal. They are designed to
keep the column wet and maintain packing structure
during storage and transportation. Save the end
caps and replace them whenever the column is not
being used.

If the installation required does not utilize an
upper end fitting which includes a frit that holds
the packing in place, be sure that some means is
provided to do this, such as the insertion of a
porous teflon plug into the top of the column.
Without this sort of device, packing/solvent
expansion during temperature or pressure changes
may allow packing material to be forced out of
the column into the injector or connecting tubing.
Always ensure that mobile phase flow is in the
direction indicated on the column.

Generally, it is not recommended that liquid chromatography columns - and particularly those with
bonded-phase packings - be used for extended periods of time at temperatures in excess of 80°C.

When shutting down the LC system, always cool the
column to room temperature under flowing conditions. If mobile phase flow is stopped at elevated
temperatures, the column performance will be de-
graded. Also, always (both during operation or
during shutdown) avoid sudden depressurization
of the columns as far as possible since this will
cause reverse-flow in the column.

Whenever the column is not in use, replace the
end caps to prevent the column from drying out.
If the column is to be stored overnight or longer,
it should be washed free of any buffer solution
and preferably stored filled with acetonitrile or
methanol or acetonitrile/methanol/water mixtures
to prevent any possibility of bacterial growth.
If it is desired to have only water in the column,
the water should contain 0.02% sodium azide to
inhibit bacterial growth.

3.94 SELECTION OF DETECTOR

The most commonly used detector is essentially an
UV spectrophotometer which is operated either at
a fixed wavelength (usually 254 nm) or permits
the selection of the wavelength at a given range.
If the properties of the compounds to be separated
are known, decisions regarding detector and wavelength are relatively easy: if there is absorption
in the detector's range, then this wavelength is
selected. The best is, of course, if the UV spectrum of the sample components is known because
this permits the selection of the optimum conditions. The use of bibliographic information is
also convenient: many times it is possible to
select the proper wavelength based on other chromatographers' work with similar compounds.

If little is known about the sample, it is necessary to use a detector which is essentially
"universal". Both variable wavelength detectors
in the far UV (210-190 nm) and refractive index
(R.I.) detectors approach this ideal. Each has
some limitations, however. The far UV detection
has limitations in the liquids which are usable
as the mobile phase in that wavelength range. The
R.I. detectors have even more restrictive requirements: it is difficult to distinguish peaks from

solvent change when one must perform gradient
elution. Given these considerations and the fact
that it is easier to use the far UV system without
having to flush the reference side of a flowcell
each time the solvent composition is changed,
many opt for performing scouting runs in the far
UV range using appropriate mobile phases.

Another point which should be considered is the
sensitivities required. If there is no way to
concentrate the sample adequately before elution,
it may be necessary to obtain the most sensitive
detector available. Examples where this may be
the case would include biochemical research and
forensic analysis, both of which have sample size
limitations. For many such applications, fluorescence spectrophotometers fulfill a real need for
high sensitivity. Another class of detectors
sometimes used when high sensitivity is required,
are the electrochemical detectors.

3.95 SCOUTING

Once the basic decisions have been made regarding
mobile phase, column, and detector, the chromatographer has the task of determining optimum
chromatographic conditions to achieve complete
separation of all components in the shortest
possible time. There are several ways which one
might approach chromatographic optimization. We
believe that the following methodology is prob-
bably one of the easiest formats for the chromatographer to follow:

Using the two mobile phase components and column
selected, complete a short (e.g., 10 minutes)
blank (no sample) linear gradient* from 10% final

---

*As discussed earlier, in gradient elution one
usually does not start with a single pure component because of the problems with adequate
pumping or mixing at the very low flow rate which
would be necessary to add the very small flows
of the second component to form the mixture
containing only a few % of it. Depending on the
instrumentation, one may start at a lower concentration mixture.

eluting component to 100%. Most likely, the baseline of this first run will be irregular; thus,
repeat the blank chromatographic gradient run
until a repeatable baseline has been obtained.
Subsequently, repeat the gradient with an
injection of filtered sample solution.

Figure 3-35 shows this type of scouting chromatogram.

Such a rapid scouting run permits one to quickly
determine (a) whether the compounds of interest
can be detected at the levels required; (b) are
they retained by, and (c) are they eluting from

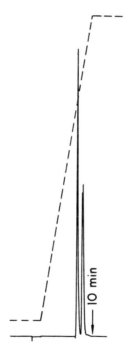

Fig. 3-35. Scouting run to develop a steroid
separation.
Column: 25 cm x 2.6 mm ID HC-ODS bonded phase.
Mobile phase: acetonitrile: water, linear gradient,
starting with 10% and ending with 100% acetonitrile.
Mobile phase flow rate: 1 mL/min. Room temperature.
UV detector at 246 nm. Broken line indicates the
gradient.
Sample: solution of hydrocortisone, hydrocortisone
acetate and cortisone acetate in acetonitrile
solution.

the column. If the answers to these questions are affirmative, then we go to the next step: selection of the mobile phase concentration, or the gradient.

Figure 3-36 shows the five general types of scouting chromatograms one may obtain. Mobile phase optimization follows from the actual type obtained.

If the peaks are closely grouped together, as in Figure 3-36/A-C, then the best separation would be obtained under isocratic conditions, i.e., using a binary mixture with constant concentration during the whole run. Concentration to be used can be estimated from the scouting run; however, it is important to realize that in any liquid chromatographic system, there is a fairly significant delay-time between the nominal concentration during a gradient, i.e., the concentration corresponding to the pump setting at that instant, and the actual concentration in the column, and typical differences can be as high as 3 minutes. Thus, the gradient program indicated by broken lines in Figures 3-35 and 3-36, represents the nominal concentration profile of the mobile phase and not the actual concentration at the corresponding time: that will be transposed parallel to the nominal profile by an amount equal to the delay time.

To obtain the actual concentration to be used, one has to calculate the actual concentration of the mobile phase when the peaks emerge from the columns. For a case such as that shown in Figures 3-36/A-C, one conveniently selects the mid-point between the peaks to which the conditions are established. In the calculation, one considers the actual concentration at this instant; this is calculated by establishing the time which had passed since the start of the gradient program and subtracting from it the delay time.

For convenience, the linear gradient is expressed as %/min. For example, if we programmed from 10% to 100% acetonitrile in 10 minutes, then the rate of gradient is (100-10)/10 = 9%/min. This value can be directly used to establish the optimum

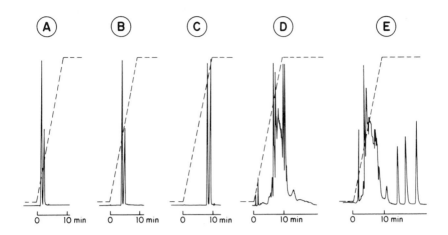

Fig. 3-36. *Possible types of scouting runs. The composition of the mobile phase is linearly programmed from 10% to 100% final eluting component. Time of the program: 10 minutes.*

mobile phase concentration. Below, the cases shown in Figures 3-36/A-C are used as examples (assuming a 3-min delay time):

Figure 3-36/A: The time corresponding to the mid-point of the peaks is 2.34 minutes. This is shorter than the 3 min delay time. Thus, one should use a 1:9 acetonitrile: water mixture as the mobile phase.

Figure 3-36/B: The time corresponding to the mid-point of the peaks is 4.7 min. Subtracting 3 min, we get 1.7 min; in this time the acetonitrile concentration changed from 10% to 10% + (1.7 x 9)% = (10 + 15.3)% = 25.3% and thus, the mobile phase should have a composition of 25.3: 74.7 acetonitrile:water.

Figure 3-36/C: The time corresponding to the mid-point of the peak is 8.7 min. Subtracting 3 min, we get 5.7 min and the corresponding acetonitrile concentration will be 10% + (5.7 x 9)% = 61.3%.

If the scouting run is similar to that seen in
Figures 3-36/D-E, i.e. the peaks elute over a wide
range of mobile phase concentration, then gradient
elution will be necessary for optimum separation.
We have three possibilities:

- If the peaks are fairly evenly distributed,
  then a single linear program is recommended.

- If the chromatogram is "crowded" toward the
  end (as in Figure 3-36/D), then one should
  have a faster change at the beginning and a
  slower one toward the end. This is achieved
  by having a convex gradient profile (cf. Figure
  1-4), or a combination of linear programs, a
  faster first, followed by a slower one.

- If the opposite is true, where more peaks
  appear at the front of the chromatogram
  (Figure 3-36/E), a concave gradient profile
  is recommended, providing a slower change
  for the first part of the separation.
  Another possibility is to use a combination
  of linear programs, first a slow and then a
  faster program; one may even use a short
  isocratic period at the start of the run or in
  between the two programs.

Another important observation in the scouting run
is the shape of the peaks. Bad tailing can be the
result of either a bad column or an ionized sample.
If columns are poorly packed or have been used at
higher pressures for a longer time, voids ("dead
volumes") may form where the mobile phase flow is
slowed down resulting in asymmetrical band broadening. The other possible reason for tailing might
be the partial ionization of the sample consisting
of acidic or basic compounds. In such a case, it
may be convenient to add modifiers to the mobile
phase. Small quantities of an acid such as acetic
acid are frequently useful to reduce tailing of
acids. Small quantities of a basic material such
as ammonium carbonate or diethylamine are often
useful to reduce tailing of basic compounds.
Alternatively, the addition of other modifiers
such as the appropriate ion pairing reagent to the
mobile phase might be applicable. The effect of

adding modifiers to the mobile phase must be studied carefully to avoid exceeding the pH limits of the column. In addition, one must realize that some modifiers will reduce column life even when the pH is controlled.

3.96 OPTIMIZATION

After the scouting run is evaluated, one can begin to optimize the final conditions of the separation. For this purpose, a series of runs are carried out with different conditions until one is satisfied that the separation could not be improved further. Since, however, each run is using up time, solvent (mobile phase) and sample, there is no justification to "shoot in the dark", by arbitrarily trying a large number of runs under varying conditions. Chromatographers are particularly tempted to do this to optimize gradient elution with fully automated instruments. Instead of this, one should rather change the conditions based on the preliminary evaluation of the scout chromatogram and then carry out a few runs with carefully selected conditions each based on the evaluation of the previous run. In this way, one can usually reach the optimum practical conditions in a relatively short time, after only a few runs.

If, based on the scouting run, isocratic operation is decided upon, one should repeat the separation, but now isocratically, with the selected concentration of the binary mobile phase and evaluate the new chromatogram. If the chromatogram is still not satisfactory, repeat it, but change the concentration by about 5%. The general rule is that if we want to shorten the chromatogram, we go up in the concentration of the stronger component while, if we want to increase retention time, then go down with strong-solvent concentration.

In cases where gradient elution is indicated, the basic decisions have already been mentioned when discussing the evaluation of the scouting run. After selecting the type of gradient, we optimize the separation by selecting the gradient rate based on the preliminary evaluation. If the original chromatogram was too crowded, we now use a slower program which usually will improve separation. Now, after obtaining a new chromatogram, we can decide on what further steps need to be taken. If there is still a "crowded" area, one would break up the program, using a slower program or even an isocratic period within the program to improve separation. On the other hand, there might be parts of the chromatogram where the separation is satisfactory and there, a faster program might be advisable.

The various liquid chromatographs are using different ways to set up a gradient program. In some instruments, the operator sets the initial and final concentration and the time the latter should be achieved; the instrument will automatically calculate the rate the pumping conditions need to be changed to achieve this goal. In other instruments, one sets the initial concentration, the rate of change, and the time of the program. For example, let us assume we want to have a gradient from 10% to 100% in 30 minutes. In the first case, we set these three values while in the second case, we set the initial concentration (10%), the time (30 min), and the rate which, in this case, is (100-10)/30 = 3%/min.

Figure 3-37 illustrates a systematic evaluation as a continuation of the situation of Figure 3-36/D. First, we repeat the analysis, but now, with a slower rate: the rate in Figure 3-36/D was 9%/min, while now, it is 3%/min. The resulting chromatogram is shown in Figure 3-37/A.

Based on this run, we presume that an isocratic period at the middle of the chromatogram would be beneficial. We want to have this at a lower concentration value so that it can be reached with a slower rate. We select 35% for the isocratic period and want to reach it in 15 minutes; this represents a rate of 1.67%/min or 1.7%/min (instruments normally permit setting increments of one tenth of a percent). Thus, depending on the instrument, we set the proper values. We also decide upon a 10-min ioscratic period and a faster final program so that the total program time is increased only by 5 minutes. The final program is

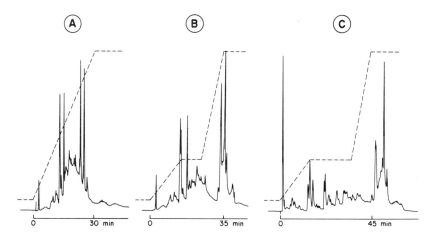

Fig. 3-37. *Optimization of analytical conditions.*
Mobile phase: tetrahydrofuran-water, programmed
from 10% THF to 100% THF. For explanation, see text.
Column: 25 cm x 2.6 mm ID HC-ODS bonded phase.
Total flow rate: 1 mL/min. UV detector qt 220 nm.
Column temperature: 50°C. Sample: alkyd melanine resin.

from 35% to 100% in 10 minutes, i.e., a rate of
6.5%/min. The resulting chromatogram is shown in
Figure 3-37/B.

Based on this chromatogram, we now decide to
double the isocratic period in order to improve
the resolution of the lump in the middle of the
chromatogram. The rest of the program is kept unchanged; thus, now, the total program time is 45
min. Figure 3-37/C shows the final chromatogram.

As seen, we have reached the final conditions in
only four runs. If the conditions would have been
preselected randomly, a very large number of runs
may have been wasted without the guarantee that
the best conditions are actually included in this
preselected set of conditions.

Part Four:
Instrumentation of Liquid Chromatography

This part of our book discusses the various principles involved in the formation of what can be called a High Performance Liquid Chromatograph. The basic components of such a system are a <u>pump</u> to propel the solvent or eluent; an <u>injection system</u> to allow application of the sample; a <u>column</u> to perform the separation; and a <u>detector</u> to determine what separation has taken place. Several accessories are often used to simplify, amplify, or increase the efficiency of the performance of the basic components. Among these are: <u>fraction collectors</u>, <u>gradient</u> and <u>recycle</u> devices, <u>column heating</u> equipment and <u>recorders</u>.

4.1 PUMPS

The pump is commonly considered the most important component in a liquid chromatography system. In choosing an instrument, the basic parameter is the pumping system. An understanding of each type and familiarity with the advantages and disadvantages of each is extremely useful and helpful. The two basic classifications are the <u>constant-pressure</u> pump and the <u>constant-flow</u> pump. In practice, these are also called the <u>positive-pressure</u> and <u>positive-flow</u> systems, respectively.

4.11 CONSTANT-PRESSURE PUMPS

The primary advantages of most constant pressure pumps are simplicity and freedom from pulsations, resulting in smooth baselines. The most simple of these are usually inexpensive, easy to operate, and easy to maintain. They suffer from several disadvantages, however. Flow rate must be monitored carefully and constantly, especially when performing either qualitative or quantitative analysis. Flow rates can change! This can happen if the solvent viscosity changes due to temperature

142

change, when columns accumulate undissolved sample components or broken-off particles of septum material, if column packing settles, or if samples dissolved in a viscous matrix are injected.

Changes of the flow rate can influence both qualitative or quantitative analysis. In qualitative analysis, component identification is primarily based on matching retention volumes. If these change as a result of flow change, especially during the analysis of complex mixtures, component location and identification becomes inaccurate or impossible. In quantitative analysis, the UV and refractive index detectors used most frequently in liquid chromatography are <u>concentration</u> <u>sensitive</u>. Changes in flow result in changes in the eluent/sample dilution ratio, or in other words, changes in concentration which show up as changes in peak area.

The most commonly available types of constant-pressure pumping systems are described below.

4.111 GAS DISPLACEMENT

Generally this drive system employs a gas cylinder connected through a regulator directly to the reservoir of the mobile phase. The gas pressure forces the liquid through the system. The liquid/ gas interface often results in absorption of gas into the liquid. This gas then comes out of solution at the end of the column, where the pressure is relieved, and is seen as a series of spikes (fast, sharp peaks) on the detector trace. If the reservoir is replaced with a long coil, the gas/liquid interface area is greatly lessened and much more of the mobile phase can be used before the gas-containing portion arrives at the detector.

The major advantages of this system are low cost, low maintenance (lack of seals to wear out), and fairly smooth detector performance. There are, however, a number of drawbacks.

The liquid capacity of these pumps is low and valves are usually included to make filling simple, since they must be refilled (and gas-containing solvent must be drained) frequently. At the same time, changing from one solvent to another is usually time-consuming and wasteful.

System pressure is limited to the pressure of the cylinder or gas reservoir, usually a maximum of 3000 psi (200 atm or 20 MPa). The use of high gas pressures in conjunction with a liquid poses a safety hazard. Liquid pressure is relatively harmless, even at extreme pressures due to its small capacity to store potential energy; thus pressures are released at the surface of the liquid instantaneously with no great expansion of the liquid. However, this is not the case when gases are used in conjunction with liquids. Hence, the chromatographer should exercise great caution when working with such a system.

4.112   GAS-AMPLIFIED PUMPS

In this type of pump, a large-bore gas piston is used to drive a small-bore liquid piston. Since the pressure on the eluent is proportional to the ratio of the cross-sectional area of the pistons, these low gas pressure sources can provide high liquid system pressures. The major advantage of such a system is its ability to pump constantly and to pump at high flow rates, if these are required, since it draws from an outside reservoir. Smooth, pulse-free detector performance is experienced between pump strokes, and solvent changeover is fairly simple.

The drawbacks of gas-amplified pumps can be summarized as follows. Since the eluent piston is small, it must be refilled frequently. This is commonly accomplished by rapidly blowing the gas piston back. A pair of check valves which allow liquid flow in one direction only, permits eluent to enter the piston chamber during the refill stroke while the closed outlet valve prevents the eluent already going to the column from being forced back into the pump. This refill operation is usually seen as a large spike on the detector. Also, the amplifier pump is relatively expensive and complex. Some maintenance is required since both pistons cycle frequently and seal wear is experienced.

A major caution when using any positive-pressure (constant-pressure) instrument involves the need to frequently check for leaks. Since the delivery system works against backpressure, if a leak develops, the pump will attempt to maintain pres-

sure and pump increasingly larger volumes of
liquid out of the area where the leak has developed. At high pressures, this may result in an
aerosol spray of hazardous solvent into spaces
occupied by humans and sources of ignition, or
both.

4.12 CONSTANT-FLOW PUMPS

Constant-flow ("positive-flow") systems are generally of two basic types: reciprocating and positive
displacement (syringe) pumps. The basic advantages
of such systems are their inherent ability to
repeat elution volume and area, regardless of
viscosity changes or column blockage or settling
occurrence, up to the pressure limit of the pump.

4.121 RECIPROCATING PUMPS

The basic reciprocating pump is the single-piston
type, the schematic of which is shown in Figure
4-1. A rotating eccentric cam forces the piston
to expel liquid through a one-way valve, the so-
called check valve. The pumping rate is usually
adjusted by controlling the distance the piston
retracts, thus limiting the amount of liquid
pushed out by each stroke.

The purpose of the check valves is to assure that
liquid moves only in one direction. Figure 4-2
shows the schematic of a check valve in open and
closed positions.

It is obvious that these pumps deliver a series
of "pulses" of the mobile phase. If it flows
through the detector in this manner, there is a
strong possibility that the detector will be
disturbed by the pulsations, especially at high
sensitivities - (Figure 4-3). Refractive index
detectors are much more sensitive to flow changes
than the more frequently used UV absorption
detectors. Thus, particularly when using the previous detector, it may be necessary to eliminate
the pulsations. Several different methods have
been developed to accomplish this. The most simple
involves placing a large (often 50 feet) coil of
narrow-bore tubing in the line between the pump

146

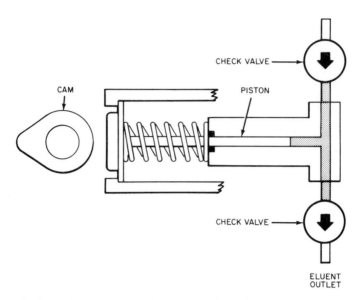

Fig. 4-1. *Schematic of a single-piston reciprocating pump.*

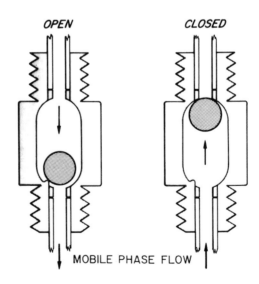

Fig. 4-2. *Operation of a check valve.*

and the column. As the pump strokes, the coil flexes, absorbing the energy of the pulsations. This type of damper holds a significant amount of liquid which must be purged during changes or

UNDAMPED PULSATIONS

DAMPED PULSATIONS
(RI DETECTOR)

Fig. 4-3. Pulsation of a mobile phase flow in recip-
rocating pumps. Top: undamped pulsations with a single
piston. Bottom: damped pulsation.

when performing gradient elution. Another variation of this is the use of a pressure gauge with
a large Bourdon tube (usually of the flowthrough
type, to prevent trapping of liquid) which also
flexes with each pulse.

A much more efficient way to provide automatic
pulse damping is the use of dual-head reciprocating pumps. The schematic of such a system is
shown in Figure 4-4. Both pump chambers are driven
by the same motor through a common cam, gears, or
hydraulic linkage; this common drive allows one
piston to pump while the other is refilling. As a
result, the two flow-profiles overlap each other
significantly reducing the pulsation downstream
of the pump; this is visualized in Figure 4-5.
Since the acceleration/deceleration profile is
somewhat non-linear, the more efficient of these
pumps use eccentrically-shaped drive-train gearing
or cams in attempting to obtain complete overlapping of the curves and obtain smooth flow.

The advantages of this pump are the unlimited
solvent reservoir allowing long-term unattended
use and quick changeover and clean out capability.
However, unless special care has been exercised

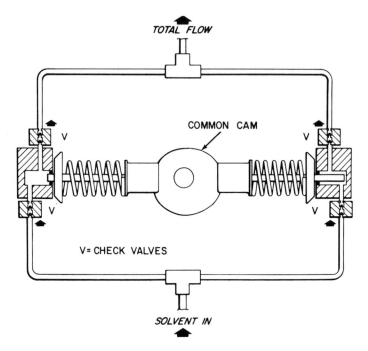

Fig. 4-4. *Schematic of a dual-head reciprocating pump.*

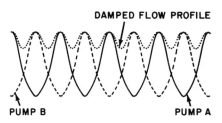

Fig. 4-5. *Flow profiles of a dual-head reciprocating pump.*

in manufacture, these pumps may have several disadvantages. There is a tendency for the in-completely compensated pulsations to be obser-vable at high refractive index detector sensi-tivities, especially at low flow rates where piston cycles are widely spread. Furthermore,

since each head has two check valves, pump reliability depends on the cleanliness of the mobile
phase and continued sealing capability of four
check valves on each cycle, with cycles normally
occurring several times per minute. When two
pumps are combined to provide mixed mobile phase
or gradient operation, eight check valves are in
operation. The drive mechanisms of some of the
more sophisticated of these pumps are often
complex and maintenance frequency may be high.

The reciprocating pumps used in Perkin-Elmer's
SERIES 1, 2 and 3B liquid chromatographs utilize
the doublehead principles described above, but
special attention has been given to eliminate the
negative aspects of this flexible, convenient
method of achieving mobile phase delivery:

- A computer-designed camshaft is used to achieve
  maximum overlap of pump strokes, resulting in
  virtually undetectable pulsation or ripple.

- Staggered inlet/outlet lines are employed to
  allow complete flushing when liquids are
  changed or if air is inadvertently drawn
  through the pump.

- Small-volume check valves are used to allow
  the pumps to function reliably at flows as
  low as 0.1 mL/min. This has the added benefit
  of providing excellent gradient reproducibility especially when programs start from
  extremely low strong-solvent concentrations.

- Each check valve has double seals with a
  second ball to act as a backup if dirt should
  interfere with the first.

- There are few moving parts, with all mainte-
  nance-requiring components (pump seals, check
  valves) readily accessible from the front of
  the instrument.

- A wide flow rate range (0.1 to 30 mL/min per
  pump) is provided without gear change, to
  allow both analytical and preparative work to
  be done on the same instrument.

4.122 SYRINGE-TYPE PUMPS

Syringe-type pumps generally consist of a cylinder that holds the mobile phase which is expelled by a piston. The piston is advanced by a motor connected through worm gears, to provide smooth pulseless flow. Figure 4-6 shows the schematic of a typical syringe pump.

Syringe pumps have a number of advantages. Pressure capability is generally quite high and maintenance is infrequent since there are no fluctuating check valves; gears are simple and strong, and since reservoir capacity is normally 250-500 mL, the pump cycles only once or twice a day in routine operation. This results in low seal and component wear.

The disadvantages of the system are the limited reservoir capacity and a slight change of flow rate when extremely high pressures compress the solvent. This compressibility is, however, relatively insignificant since the highest rate noted is 4% compression at 6000 psi or a practically undetectable change of 0.04 mL/min. When compared to the effect a change in viscosity has on a constant pressure pump, (3x increase in viscosity would reduce flow from 1mL/min to 0.33 mL/min), the effect of compressibility becomes academic.

The pump shown in Figure 4-6 has an exit line up through the center of the piston. This allows the cylinder to be removed and replaced easily for rapid, complete, cleanout and changeover. The importance of ability to completely clean and dry the system cannot be overemphasized. In several modes of liquid chromatography, even the slightest trace of contamination between liquids of widely different characteristics can result in irregular or unpredictable column or detector performance. Two of these pumps are often combined and driven through an electronic system which provides mixed mobile phase and gradient-programming operation, or drive can be arranged synchronously so that one pump can be refilled while the other is operating to obtain continuous elution.

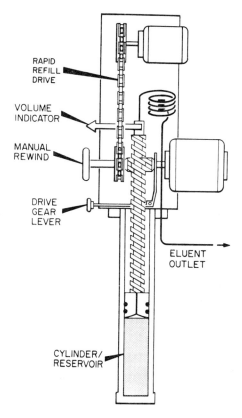

RAPID
REFILL
DRIVE

VOLUME
INDICATOR

MANUAL
REWIND

DRIVE
GEAR
LEVER

ELUENT
OUTLET

CYLINDER/
RESERVOIR

Fig. 4-6. Schematic of a positive-displacement syringe pump.

4.13 BLENDING AND MIXING MOBILE PHASE COMPONENTS

In many of the modes of modern liquid chromatography, it becomes readily apparent that the most practical system for the delivery of the mobile phase are those which can combine several liquids in different proportions at the command of the operator. This blending capability greatly speeds the process of selecting the optimum eluent mixture required for isocratic analysis and becomes absolutely necessary when programming of the mobile phase composition ("gradient elution") is required. These techniques have been discussed earlier from the point of chromatography; now we shall treat them from the point of instrumentation.

152

The two primary methods of blending the mobile phase components are known as high-pressure mixing and low-pressure mixing. The principles of the two methods are shown in Figure 4-7.

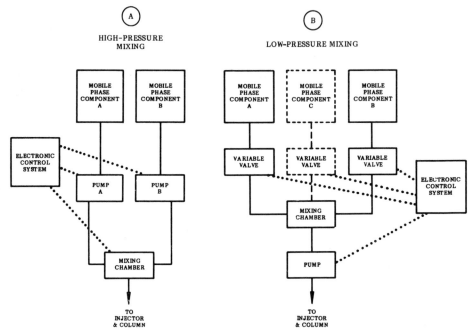

Fig. 4-7. *Principles of the two primary methods of blending the mobile phase components.*

4.131 HIGH-PRESSURE MIXING

In high-pressure mixing systems (Figure 4-7/A), individual pumps are used to provide each different liquid. The outlet of each pump is either connected to a mixing connector (usually referred to as a "T" since there are normally two inlet lines and one outlet line) or to a mixing chamber. In these, the two flows are blended en route to the injector and column. In other words, mixing is accomplished on the high-pressure side of the pumps.

Most modern liquid chromatography systems utilizing this principle include pump-drive electronics which control the pumping speed. Blending is achieved through adjustment of a master control. The flow rate which always represents the combined (total) output of both pumps is selected, then the dividing control adjusted to provide the desired ratio of the two components. These controls are commonly calibrated to read out percentage of strong component in the mixture.

On Perkin-Elmer, and many other liquid chromatographs, the stronger component is considered Component A; thus, the mixing control is labeled "%A in A+B". When a given %A is dialed in, the mixing electronics automatically divide the output signal between the two pumps; Pump A (strong component) receives the percentage of signal called for in the control indicator, and Pump B (weaker component) receives the remainder of the signal, so that the total output of both pumps always equals the preselected flow rate.

Figure 4-7/A shows the mixing of two mobile-phase components. It is also possible to prepare ternary mobile phases by utilizing three separate pumps. Each of these pumps will then deliver a separate solvent into the mixing chamber.

Among the advantages of high-pressure mixing are the ability to achieve precise control and repeatability of mobile phase mixtures to within 0.1% levels, rapid response to changes in concentration, and the ability to utilize each pump separately in the event of problems with one, or if separate isocratic pumping systems are required.

4.132 LOW-PRESSURE MIXING

In low-pressure mixing systems, mixing is accomplished prior to the pump, at its low-pressure side and the overall flow rate is controlled by a single pump. Blending of the mobile-phase components is accomplished with controls which are calibrated in somewhat the same manner as those used for high-pressure mixers - that is, controlling the percentage of strong component - though some systems allow the mixing of three liquids. In general, two types of blending systems are used.

In the first case, proportioning valves, normally solenoid operated, are used to deliver the individual liquids. The controller simply divides the signal according to the percentage of each compo-

nent and each valve is opened for the proper
period of time. Usually the valves deliver the
individual liquids into a mixing chamber (Figure
4-7/B) which then feeds the blend to the pump
supplying the binary or ternary mobile phase to
the injector and column. In some systems, the
mixing chamber may be missing and the valves feed
the mobile-phase components through a mixing
connector directly to the high-pressure pump.

The primary advantage of such systems is that they
offer the ability to blend two or more liquids
without the increased expense and maintenance of
additional pump(s), although the complex valve-
actuating systems and valves required almost
negate this.

The second type of low-pressure mixing systems
utilize separate low-pressure pumps instead of the
proportioning valves to deliver the individual
liquids to the mixing chamber. The advantage of
such a system is the very precise control and high
repeatability of mobile phase mixtures. However,
the fact that now, three or four pumps are used in
the system represents an increased expense and
added burden in maintenance.

4.133 PROGRAMMING THE MOBILE PHASE
COMPOSITION

In gradient elution, the concentration of the
mobile phase is varied during a run. There are two
possibilities: the change in concentration is
linear with time or it is not linear. In the
latter case, the plot describing the program might
be convex or concave. Figure 1-4 shows the three
types of programs. Instruments which are capable
of mixing liquids for the mobile phase are also
capable of carrying out gradient elution automatically.

A linear program is described by four variables
(Figure 4-8): the initial and final concentration
(%) of Component A in the mixed mobile phase, the
rate of program (%/min) and the length (time) of
the program. Three of these four fully describe
the program; in practice, the instruments permit
the setting of the two concentrations and either

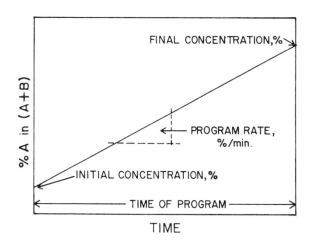

Fig. 4-8. The variables of a gradient elution program.

the time or the rate of the program. The electronic control system will then automatically set either the rate or the time of the program. The third possibility would be to set the initial concentration, the time and the rate of the program; however, this mode is not frequently used in practice.

More sophisticated instruments permit multi-level programming, that is, to have two or more linear programs with different rates and intermittent isocratic periods. With less sophisticated instruments, this must be done manually: set the first program, then, when it is finished and while the separation is still in progress, set the second program, etc.

The situation with curved gradient profiles depends on the particular instrument. Some less convenient programmers require step-by-step entry of multiple percentage vs. time plateaus to approach curved gradient profiles while in more sophisticated systems, one can select from a number of programmed profiles. For example, Figure 4-9 presents the profiles possible in the microcomputer-controlled pump module of the Perkin-Elmer SERIES 3B liquid chromatographs.

The curves in Figure 4-9 are described by the following equation:

$$A_i\% = (A_1\%) + [(A_2\%) - (A_1\%)] \ (\frac{t_i}{T})^n \qquad (18a)$$

where $A_i\%$ is the concentration of component A in the binary mobile phase (A+B) at t_i time;

$A_1\%$ is the initial concentration of component A at the start of the program (t_i=0);

$A_2\%$ is the final concentration of component A at the end of the program (t_i=T); and

T is the length of the program expressed as time.

The value of n, the exponent of the equation is equal to the numeral written on the curves in Figure 4-9. As seen, it is a whole number for concave curves while it is a fraction for convex gradient programs.

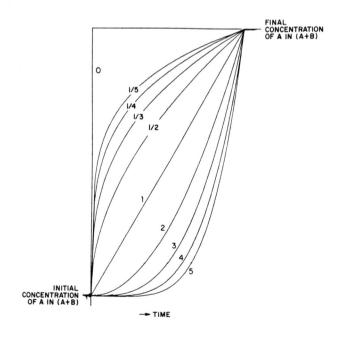

Fig. 4-9. Preprogrammed gradient profiles used in a Perkin-Elmer liquid chromatograph.

In the actual instruments, one has to set the initial and final concentrations, the time of the program and select which program profile is desired. This is done by certain keys corresponding to the various exponent values.

If n=1, we have a linear program described as

$$A_i\% = (A_1\%) + \frac{(A_2\% - (A_1\%)}{T} t_i \qquad (18b)$$

where the fraction in the right-hand side of the equation is the rate of the program.

Naturally, in sophisticated instruments where various programs can be combined, curved programs can also be included together with linear programs and isocratic periods.

The absolute most important consideration in gradient elution is that the whole program - a simple single as well as a complex multistage program - can be exactly reproduced upon command since innaccurate gradient repetition can contribute to significant qualitative and quantitative errors.

4.14 CHOICE OF THE PUMPING SYSTEM

The ideal pump would be completely pulse-free, with an unlimited reservoir, have instantaneous clean-out characteristics and never need maintenance. Naturally, such a pump does not exist or, if it did, then its cost would place it outside the possibilities of analytical instrumentation. Therefore, in choosing a pump, the potential user must consider both his requirements and his budget. If the majority of use requires high volumes of mobile phase, a simple reciprocating pump may be used since high solvent requirements generally imply heavy sample loading where detectors are run at nominal settings and the pulsations are not noted. On the other hand, a good general-purpose research-grade analytical instrument should be able to cope with constantly improving column technology (which may occasionally require pressures in the order of 3000-4000 lb/sq.in), should be able to be operated at the highest detector sensitivities (thus, be pulse-free), and

should be able to provide flow rates commensurate
with the inner diameter of the most efficient
columns (0.5 to 6 mL/min). In addition to this,
the system must be inert to the acids, bases, and
organic solvents required to dissolve, separate,
and elute the samples.

The double-head type reciprocating pumps with
high-pressure dual-pump liquid mixing capability -
such as those marketed by Perkin-Elmer - fulfill
both requirements. Their solvent capacity is for
all practical purposes unlimited as compared e.g.,
to the syringe pumps having only a capacity of
about 250 - 500 mL; they require very little maintenance, have a small size and relatively low cost.
Also, they have great flexibility in being capable
of operating in a wide variety of applications,
from the most simple isocratic analysis to complex
multi-stage gradient-elution programs and from
manual sample injection to utilization in automated, unattended around-the-clock operation.

4.15   PROBLEMS ENCOUNTERED IN PUMPING LIQUIDS

The common problems encountered in pumping liquids
in liquid chromatography are solvent degassing,
corrosion, and compressibility. Compressibility
has already been discussed in Section 4.122
(syringe pumps); since its influence is minor,
we shall not deal with it further. The two other
problems, however, need further analysis.

4.151   DEGASSING

As previously noted, when the mobile phase contains
excessive gas which remains dissolved at the
pressure produced by the column, the gas may come
out of the solution at the column exit or in the
detector, resulting in spikes or baseline drift.
Spikes are created by microscopic bubbles which
change the nature of the flowing stream making it
heterogeneous while drift may occur as these microscopic bubbles gradually collect and combine in
the detector cell, which is often the lowest-
pressure area in the system. Under ordinary cir-
cumstances, liquids which have been delivered and
stored in closed containers do not carry high

levels of gas and can be used without degassing. The more polar liquids, such as alcohols and water, tend to hold the most unacceptable gas levels. A good rule-of-thumb is to attempt to use the material without degassing, especially if the sample level permits a detector sensitivity of 0.10 optical density, or higher, and/or a RI sensitivity of x4, or higher, on the commonly available units. If outgassing occurs, it will be seen as a series (often highly regular) of sharp peaks on the recorder. If a fluorescence detector is used, it is important to degas since dissolved oxygen can quench fluorescence, essentially reducing sensitivity or introducing excessive baseline noise.

If needed, degassing may be accomplished by one of the following methods or their combination:

- Heating the liquid until boiling occurs.

- Subjecting the liquid to a source of vacuum. CAUTION: even a simple aspirator can cause the collapse of an ordinary flask; use only heavy-walled flasks.

- Placing the container of liquid in an ultra-sonic bath, or inserting an ultrasonic probe in it.

- Bubbling a fine stream of helium through the liquid; helium has the unique ability to dissolve other gases out of the solutions in which they are entrained.

4.152 CORROSION

Most commercially available instruments are con-structed of Type 316 stainless steel. This material represents the best compromise of corrosion resis-tance, workability, strength, and cost. It is inert to all bases, all organic liquids and most nonhalogenated acids at pH values above 2.0. Type 316 stainless steel is, however, extremely vulner-able to contact with halogenated acids, as HCl, even at concentrations as low as 0.01 normal. When attempting to convert a thin-layer or (glass) column chromatographic method to HPLC, substitute

a harmless acid such as nitric, boric, or acetic
for halogens. Ion-exchange systems should be
monitored carefully for discolored eluent especially when small particle packings that exhibit
high back pressure (2500+ psi) are used, since
several researchers have observed highly accel-
erated corrosive reactions at these pressures with
some buffer systems.

4.2 SAMPLE INTRODUCTION

The method of sample introduction is of primary
importance in HPLC. If an inefficient injection
device causes sample components to be applied as
a long, wide band, the best columns available
cannot yield sharp narrow peaks. The primary
consideration in injector design is the need to
provide a low-volume, completely swept area to
avoid sample diffusion and exponential dilution.
As instrument and column technology provide
analytical systems which offer extremely rapid,
efficient separations of incredibly small amounts
of material, the demands made on the injection
system become tremendous. Therefore, while inject-
tion through a septum has historically been the
most frequently used method of sample introduction,
septum injectors are rapidly being replaced by
septumless syringe-injector valves.

4.21 SYRINGE INJECTION THROUGH A SEPTUM

Septum injection is inexpensive, flexible, and
easily performed. Ideally, the sample is placed at
the top of the column so it can be swept into the
column without back-mixing and subsequent band
spreading. The injector shown in Figure 4-10
illustrates such a system. The particular injector
shown contains a simple but impressive feature: the
domed septum retainer. The domed retainer allows
the system backpressure to force the flexible
silicone rubber septum up into the hollowed portion.
This flexing causes the bottom of the hole made by
the needle to close more rapidly than the top when
the needle is withdrawn, effectively sealing the
system. When this injector is used, 50-60 injections are routinely made into ordinary silicone
rubber septums, often at pressures as high as 2000
lb/sq. in.

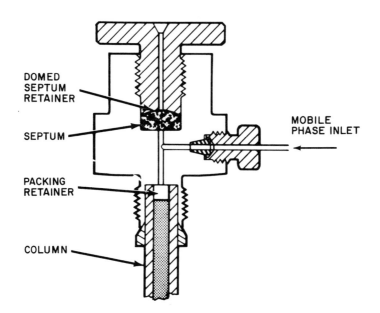

Fig. 4-10. Schematic of an injection port for syringe injection.

The capacity of the most commonly used syringe is 10 microliters. Needle length or injection depth must be regulated according to the instrument since inserting the needle into the top of the column usually results in a plugged syringe and no injection of sample.

4.22 STOPFLOW INJECTION

It is difficult to force more than 25-50 microliters into a high pressure system utilizing 2-3 mm ID columns, thus, it is a frequent practice to inject smaller, more highly concentrated samples when scaling up analyses, or to perform stopflow injection. Stopflow is accomplished in several ways, but primarily they all utilize a removeable cap at the entrance to the column. Flow is stopped, the cap removed, sample inserted (normally with a syringe), then the cap is installed and pump started. This method is frequently used when especially high pressure systems are being operated, since most septa will not withstand more than 3000 lb/sq. in.

A valve placed immediately before the column greatly simplifies the stopflow procedure. The use of such

a valve also greatly increases the efficiency of
septum injection. Closing the valve immediately
prior to injection allows injections to be made at
low pressure, greatly increasing accuracy since
there is less tendency for the sample to be forced
up past the plunger. In addition to this, septum
and syringe life is greatly extended. If the entire
valve-closing, injecting, valve-opening procedure
is carried out by simultaneously switching the
pump(s) off and on at the same time as the valves
are actuated, there is little system upset. As a
side benefit of the procedure, the detector pen
may make a spike when the valve is reopened,
marking the point of injection accurately and
precisely.

In spite of all the advantages, however, stopflow
injection, even using valves to stop the mobile
phase flow, is still a slow, laborious method
which requires absolute adherence to technique to
yield any measure of precision at all.

4.23 VALVE INJECTION

Despite its flexibility and adaptability, septum
injection has several drawbacks; notably, the
pressure restrictions mentioned in the previous
section and, of more practical significance, the
absolute dependence on operator technique when
used in quantitative analysis. High-pressure valves
are available to overcome the former objection. By
their very nature, injection valves provide highly
reproducible sample application. While a skilled
operator using a syringe may approach an injection
precision of +1% relative standard deviation, 1.5
to 2.0% is more common. A good valve injector
routinely allows a precision of + 0.5%. The only
precaution is that cleanliness be observed so that
dirt is not injected or precipitates are not
allowed to form which might minutely scratch the
sealing surfaces during successive cycles. This
leads to eventual valve leakage and failure.

The sample introduction valves used in practice
can be divided into two groups: simple loop valves
and septumless syringe injector valves.

4.231 LOOP VALVES

Though they are available from several suppliers,
most loop valves can be divided into two groups:
external and internal. In the external loop valves,
a section of small diameter tubing serves as the
"loop" to hold the sample while in the internal
valves an internally bored section contains the
sample.

In general, the length of tubing used in the
external valves for the loop is chosen according
to the desired sample amount. The schematic of a
typical external loop valve is shown in Figure
4-11. The valve has two positions: the "bypass"
or "fill" position during which the sample is
introduced into the loop and the "inject" position
when the content of the loop is flushed into the
column. While in the bypass position, the mobile
phase flows from the pump directly to the column
through an interior orifice. This is necessary to
maintain flow, establish equilibrium, and allow
balancing of the detector prior to sample introduction.

While the loop is bypassed by the mobile phase
flow, the sample loop is filled with the liquid
sample to be analyzed. Normally, a large volume
syringe is used to force an excess of sample

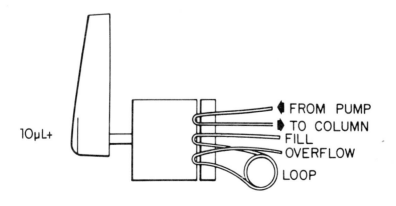

Fig. 4-11. Schematic of an external-loop-type sample
introduction valve.

through the valve. Some researchers consider it
more practical to draw the sample into the valve
by holding the outlet tube in the sample and
pulling the syringe plunger back. The overflow
port and syringe are observed to assure that any
bubbles are flushed out.

After the sample is introduced into the loop and
the column conditions are properly adjusted, the
valve is switched to the "inject" position. This
allows the mobile phase to flow through the sample
loop, washing the material onto the column.

External loop valves are commonly used in preparative chromatography; the introduced sample size is
normally a minimum of 10 μL, but may be as high as
2 mL. If smaller samples are to be introduced,
this may be accomplished by filling the loop only
partially with the sample introduced into it with
a syringe. However, in this case, the repeatability
of introduced volume depends on the operator's
skill. Therefore, for the introduction of small
sample volumes, the internal valves are preferred.
These are based on the same principles as the
external loop valves except that the loop is
replaced by an internally bored section - with a
smaller volume - which now contains the sample.
This flowthrough hole is machined directly into
the rotor of the valve and thus, has a fixed
volume, typically 3 μL.

A general requirement for a sampling valve is that
there should be no rapid changes in diameter which
would leave unflushed corners and trapped pockets
of sample.

4.232 SEPTUMLESS SYRINGE INJECTION VALVES

The most convenient and flexible valves, by far,
are those which allow "septumless syringe injection". These injectors allow the operator to
vary injection size without the necessity for
shutting the system down and making plumbing
changes. They allow injection offline, at ambient
pressures, thus can be used for continuous operation in high-pressure systems. The seals typically withstand 5000-6000 psi pressures.

Septumless syringe injection valves exist in two
types: the schematics of both are shown in Figure
4-12. The more sophisticated type shown in the
top drawing (e.g., Perkin-Elmer type 7105) includes
a bypass-line to prevent inducing a pressure surge
when injection is made at high backpressures, since
some workers feel that these injection surges may
be harmful to columns. However, it has recently
been felt that this bypass line may induce some
problems at <u>low</u> pressures. Therefore, the valve
with a more simplified construction (bottom
drawing in Figure 4-21) - such as e.g. Perkin-Elmer
type 7125 - is becoming one of the most frequently
used systems. This valve allows injection of from
0.1 to 20 microliters without plumbing changes.
If larger samples are desired, a longer (larger
volume) loop can be readily installed.

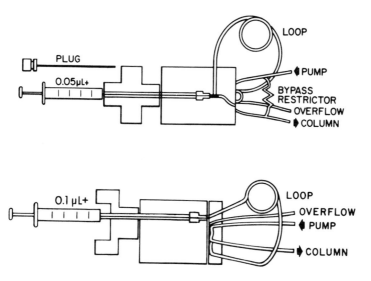

Fig. 4-12. Schematics of various types of septumless
syringe injector valves. Top: valve with a bypass line.
Bottom: simplified valve without a bypass line.

Since both types of valves reverse the flow when
the valve is rotated - allowing the last portion
injected to be the first portion to be pumped onto
the column - small amounts of material can be
injected into valves equipped with large loops
without danger of sample dilution and peak broadening.

4.3 COLUMNS

It has been shown that there are various satisfactory methods of transportating the solvent and
injecting the sample, and it will be shown that
there may be several equally satisfactory methods
of observing (detecting) the results of the separation; but for any given separation, there is
usually only one type of column which provides
good results. Let us not forget the old saying:
"the column is the heart of a chromatograph"

The various types of column packings and their
role in separation have been discussed earlier in
this book. Here, we shall restrict ourselves to
questions relating to the physical column, that
is, the tubing and connections.

4.31 THE COLUMN TUBING

Today, column material is normally Type 316 stainless steel, once again chosen because it offers
the best compromise of cost, workability, and
corrosion resistance. As already mentioned in the
previous part, most commercial columns available
today have internal diameters of either 2.6-3 mm
or 4.6-5 mm. Most leading manufacturers obtain a
great amount of interchangeability between column
sizes without excessive fitting replacement by
supplying columns with a variety of internal
diameters, but a uniform 1/4 in. outside diameter.
Naturally, preparative columns have larger diameters: usual O.D. values are 3/8 - 5/8 in.,
corresponding to internal diameters of 6.4-12.7 mm,
respectively.

4.32 COLUMN HARDWARE

Most modern liquid chromatography plumbing is
performed with compression fittings such as
Swagelok ®, Parker-Hannifin ®, Gyrolok ®, etc.
These offer a great deal of flexibility, can be
connected and disconnected frequently without loss
of sealing power, are commonly available, and may
be used without special seating and flanging tools
allowing users to install, maintain, modify, and
improvise equipment. Great care should be taken in

the choice of end fittings, connectors, and unions, however, since inclusion of rapid diameter changes, corners, and other unswept areas in a system can destroy a good separation. It is best to obtain the above parts from a reputable liquid chromato- graph manufacturer since most of these companies offer fittings which are specifically made for LC.

Many reducing unions and column end fittings incorporate special devices designed to hold pack- ings in place and/or prevent their flowing into the detector or detector tubing. The most fre- quently used of these consist of fine porous stain- less steel fritted filter discs, usually with an average opening of 2 μm. These may be forced into the ends of columns or may be in the connector or end fitting. The important point is that the fritted disc must be tightly fitted to avoid occurrence of large-diameter spaces at the edge where the disc contacts the wall. An additional benefit of the frit is derived from the fact that it fills what otherwise might be a large empty area in conver- sion zones thus, the sample cannot diffuse, cross- mix, or undergo other efficiency-killing effects when passing through these areas.

4.33 CONNECTOR TUBING

Connector tubing must be of low cross section to hold separated components in narrow bands as they are transferred from column-to-column, from column-to-detector, or from detector-to-detector when mounted in series. Tubing having an internal diameter in excess of 0.634 mm (0.025 in) can allow peak mixing and band broadening and it is good practice to use tubing no larger than 0.38 mm (0.015 in) in areas where sample is to be trans- ported. On the other hand, care must be exercised when tubing with an internal diameter of 0.25 mm (0.010 in) or less is used since these very narrow tubes may be easily plugged by random packing particles or sample precipitation.

A complete guide to column connection is included in Appendix I of this booklet.

4.4 DETECTORS

4.41 INTRODUCTION

In early liquid chromatography, mobile phase flow
was disconnected before the first separated compounds would have eluted. Thus, the chromatographic
column contained the separated compounds in the
form of colored rings. If quantitative evaluation
was necessary, the column had to be very carefully
separated into fractions so that the packings
containing the various colored rings remained together. Now, the pure sample component had to be
extracted from the particles, filtered off, and
then the amount of the component determined by
various means.

In the second part of the 1930's, this very tedious
method was gradually replaced by a more advanced
technique, having the mobile phase continuously
flowing through the column and gradually eluting
each separated fraction. The column eluent was
collected in small volumes and each fraction was
then analyzed for the individual compound(s)
present in it. This was still a very elaborate
method requiring many hours of work, evaporating
the solvent from each fraction, analyzing the
remaining sample components and then plotting
amount vs. eluent volume in order to obtain the
chromatogram which then, in turn, permits the calculation of sample concentration.

The introduction of flowthrough detectors represented a major breakthrough on which modern liquid
chromatography could evolve. Such detection was
first applied by the group of Tiselius, in Sweden
in 1940, by continuously measuring the refractive
index of the column effluent. It is safe to say
that the evolution of automated flowthrough detectors represented the leading reason for the emergence of liquid chromatography as a modern analytical technique. Current LC detectors have wide
dynamic range normally allowing both analytical
and preparative scale runs on the same instrument.
They have high sensitivities often allowing the
detection of nanograms of material, and the better
models are very flexible, allowing rapid conver-

sion from one mobile phase to another and from one mode to another.

The primary design concept of all LC detectors is that they be on-stream monitors. That is, they are almost always used under continuous flow conditions and the sample is always dissolved in the eluent during detection. Typically, actual sample is only present in a 1:100 ratio in the detector, but in trace analysis, the ratio can be as high as 1:10,000! In considering the actual amount of material which is sensed in a 10-micro-liter cell at any given moment, the analyst must gain an appreciation for the quality and sensi-tivity of these units.

When compared with gas chromatography, there is a major difference in the question associated with detection in liquid chromatography: while in GC, the mobile phase (the carrier gas) normally does not represent any concern; in liquid chromato-graphy, the eluting mobile phase is a factor which must always be considered, at least with the most frequently used detector types.

In spite of all the advances achieved in the last two decades, liquid chromatography detection still has one major drawback: to-date, these is no reliable, easy-to-use detector which is sensitive to all materials in all mobile phase systems. In other words, there is no equivalent of the thermal conductivity detector of gas chromatography which, when used with the proper carrier gas, will detect almost any eluting compound. For this reason, the liquid chromatographer must expect to eventually use more than one type of detector. Fortunately, there are several straight-forward criteria avail-able to aid in choosing the proper detector.

Below, we shall summarize the principles of the most frequently used liquid chromatography detec-tors and various questions associated with them. For a more detailed discussion, the reader is referred to the general liquid chromatography textbooks or specifically, to the report of R.D. Conlon or the book of R.P.W. Scott:

R.D. Conlon, Liquid Chromatography Detectors.
Analytical Chemistry 41 (4), 107A-114A
(1969).

R.P.W. Scott, Liquid Chromatography Detectors.
Elsevier, Amsterdam, Oxford and New York
(1977).

4.42 BASIC DETECTOR REQUIREMENTS

4.421 CELL EFFICIENCY

As mentioned, practically all present-day LC detectors are on-stream systems, continuously monitoring
certain characteristics (refractive index, UV
absorption at a given wavelength, etc.) of the
column effluent in a flowthrough cell. Modern LC
systems employ fairly low flow rates and provide
high resolution in a short time. Thus, it is very
important to have well designed cells in which the
separated bands remain separated and do not widen.
Otherwise, the achievements of one part of the
system would be counteracted by the other: it is
useless to employ a column which can separate a
dozen components in two minutes if the components
are allowed to mix again in the detector.

In practice, the term cell efficiency is used to
define the ability of a detector cell to maintain
the eluted components as sharp, separate bands with
little or no dilution in the cell. This dilution
would be seen as peak broadening, peak height
reduction, peak overlapping and/or peak tailing
in the chromatogram:

• Peak broadening will occur because, due to
longitudinal diffusion, the same amount of
solute will occupy a larger mobile phase
volume, thus increasing the peak width.

• Peak height is reduced because the peak area
is proportional to the total sample amount:
if the amount is unchanged, but the peak width
increases, then the peak height must be
reduced.

• Peak overlapping occurs because while the
maximum of the peaks remains at the same

position, their width increases so much that they actually enter into each other.

● Peak tailing might occur if parts of the cell are inefficiently flushed by the mobile phase stream. Thus, solute molecules entering these areas will only be able to leave them again, slowly.

Most of the present day liquid chromatography detectors utilize low-volume cells which are efficiently flushed to prevent band broadening and tailing. A measure of the efficiency of these cells is the so-called instrument bandwidth.

The instrument bandwidth, expressed in microliters, is the minimum peak volume which the detector produces no matter how small the sample volume introduced into the detector. For this purpose, it is more useful to calculate the bandwidth corresponding to the peak width at base (w_b) than to the peak width at half height (w_h).

4.422 NOISE AND DRIFT

The peaks one obtains in a chromatogram represent deflection of the recorder pen from the baseline. If the peaks are fairly large, one has no problem in clearly distinguishing them. However, the smaller the peaks, the more important that the baseline be smooth, free of noise, and drift.

Baseline noise is the short time variation of the baseline from a straight line and appears as a series of small peaks, waves, and vertical spikes sometimes called "grass". Noise is normally measured "peak-to-peak": i.e., the distance from the top of one such small peak to the bottom of the next, is measured vertically. Sometimes, noise is averaged over a specified period of time. The practical significance of noise is that this is the factor which limits detector sensitivity: in trace analysis, the operator must be able to distinguish between noise spikes and component peaks. A practical limit for this is a 2x signal-to-noise ratio: the component peak must be at least twice the height of the average noise. Figure 4-13 illustrates this, indicating the

172

noise level of a baseline (measured at highest
detector sensitivity) and the smallest peak which
can be unequivocally detected.

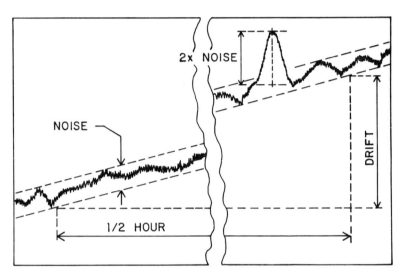

Fig. 4-13. *Definition of noise, drift, and smallest
detectable peak.*

Besides low noise which is a short-time characteristic of a detector, an additional requirement is
that the baseline should deviate as little as
possible from a horizontal line. This deviation
is called the drift. It is usually measured for a
specified time, e.g., 1/2 hour or one hour. Figure
4-13 also illustrates the meaning of drift.

4.43 THE REFRACTIVE INDEX DETECTOR

4.431 PRINCIPLES

The refractive index (RI) detector is the most
universal detector in common use.

A fixed refractive index is a definite physical
characteristic of every compound. Some difficulty
occasionally arises, however, in selecting a mobile
phase system that is compatible with the separation
mode and system components, but which is different
from that of the sample. Since the detection prin-

ciple involves balancing the system at a constant
flow of pure mobile phase and measuring the change
in refractive index as eluting sample is added to
the mobile phase, it is obvious that the greater
the RI difference between sample and mobile phase,
the larger the imbalance will become. Thus, the
highest sensitivity is obtained when the widest
difference exists between sample and mobile phase.
On the other hand, in complex mixtures, sample
components may cover a wide range of refractive
index values and some may closely match that of
the mobile phase, becoming invisible to the detector. An additional detriment is the requirement
for rebalancing the detector each time there is a
slight change in the mobile phase composition.
This factor is often severely limiting since it
renders the RI detector unusable in the practice of
gradient elution, where mobile phase constitution
or concentration is changed during the analysis to
effect the separation. It is possible to attempt
to form high and low-polarity solvent mixtures
carefully blended to have equal RI's, but this is
extremely difficult unless only low detector sensitivities are to be used.

Two basic types of RI detectors are in common use
today. Both require the use of a two-path cell
where the sample-containing side is constantly
compared with the non-sample-containing reference
side.

4.432 DEFLECTION DETECTORS

The optical schematic of the deflection, or Snell's
Law detector is shown in Figure 4-14. This detector, sold primarily by Waters Associates, Inc.,
Milford, MA., utilizes the deflection principle of
refractometry, where the deflection of a light
beam is measured when the composition of the sample
path changes in relation to the reference side, as
eluting sample moves through the system. When no
sample is present in the cell, the light passing
through both sides is focused on the detector. As
sample elutes through one side, the changing angle
of refraction moves the beam. This results in a
change in the signal going to the detector which
unbalances it. The extent of unbalance (which can

174

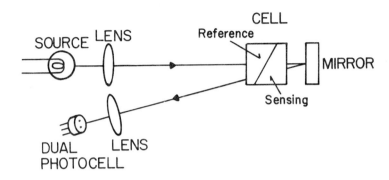

*Fig. 4-14.   Optical schematic of a deflection-type
refractive index detector.*

then be related to the concentration of the sample)
is recorded on a strip chart recorder.

The advantages of this type of detector are low
sensitivity to dirt and air bubbles in the cells,
and the ability to cover the entire refractive
index range from 1.000 to 1.75 with a single,
easily balanced cell. The disadvantages are the
high price and, as a result of the critical place-
ment of the cell in the center of the optics, a
general disability to easily remove and clean or
replace the cell when filming or clogging occurs.

4.433   REFLECTIVE (FRESNEL) DETECTORS

The second common refractive index detector
utilizes the Fresnel principle. Figure 4-15 shows
the optical schematic of this type of detector.
Here, the light beam is focused on and reflected
from both the liquid-prism cell interfaces and a
polished backplate (which forms the rear surface
of both sample and reference cells) onto the
detecting photocell. As the intrusion of sample
into the one cell causes light to be refracted at
a different angle, this light changes in intensity
rather than position, with the unbalance once
again being detected as a change in electrical
energy. Here, too, this difference between sample-
cell signal and reference-cell signal is output
to a recorder or data handling system as a milli-
volt change.

The major advantage of this type of detector is a higher potential sensitivity since the optics allow a higher concentration of signal in a particular RI range than is possible in wide-range detectors. Other advantages include the ability to operate at extremely low flow rates with very low-volume cells, easy cell accessibility, and low cost. Its disadvantages are the need for changing prisms to accomodate either high or low RI solvents and the need to manually adjust the optical path when making solvent changes.

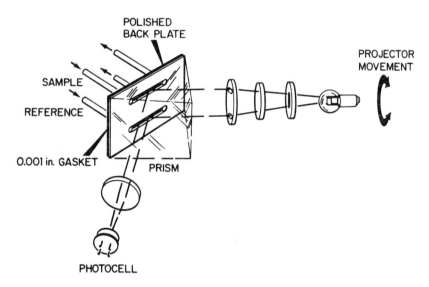

Fig. 4-15. Optical schematic of the Fresnel-type refractive index detector.

4.434 INFLUENCES ON DETECTOR SENSITIVITY

The refractive index of a compound is a function of its molecular density. Change in density is reflected as a change in the RI, thus a refractometer is sensitive to changes in concentration of sample or solvent, pressure, or temperature, since all of these effect changes in density. A refractive index detector suitable for use in liquid chromatography should be sensitive to changes as small as 10^{-7} RI units (corresponding to a concentration change of 1 ppm). Presence of dissolved air, changes in solvent composition, improper mixing and column

bleed will contribute to baseline drift. A typical
organic liquid used as mobile phase will undergo
a change of 1×10^{-6} RI unit under a pressure
change of 15 lb/in.^{2} and a change of 600×10^{-6}
RI units with a 1°C temperature variation, thus it
is obvious that these conditions must be closely
controlled, especially temperature. To operate at
high sensitivities, a RI detector must usually have
a water bath, capable of holding temperatures within $\pm$ 0.01°C, connected to the detector head or,
alternately, a massive internal heat sink, to
stabilize against temperature effects. Commercial
detectors normally include a length of narrow-bore
tubing in the inlet side to allow temperature
stabilization of eluting material prior to its
emergence in the cell.

4.435   SAMPLE SIZE AND CELL VOLUME
REQUIREMENTS

Assuming that the sample will become diluted by
about 100 to 1 with the mobile phase in the column
(this is a general rule-of-thumb in all LC separations) and assuming that a 10^{-5} difference in RI
can be readily detected, the typical sample size,
in milligrams, will be roughly the reciprocal of
the difference in RI between mobile phase and
sample.

Many commercial units offer a variety of cell sizes
to accomodate particular requirements. The chromatographer who commonly uses large-bore columns (8 mm
and wider) will normally employ large sample sizes
and, therefore, requires a large-volume cell (typically, 20 µL) while the analyst who routinely
performs analytical work on narrow-bore columns
requires a small-volume cell (typically 5 µL) with
high sensitivity and rapid response. The use of a
large-volume cell for low-volume work will, of
course, result in excessive peak broadening, while
the use of a low-volume cell with large sample
sizes may result in overloading of the cell, mis-
shapen peaks and consequent inaccurate quantitation.

4.44 ULTRAVIOLET/VISIBLE SPECTROSCOPIC DETECTORS

4.441 PRINCIPLES

When various functional groups are exposed to radiation, they experience electronic excitation which results from the absorption of energy at wavelengths specific to the functional group. This energy promotes electron motion from a ground state to a higher energy state. The consequent absorption of energy results in loss of light from a beam which has been projected through the sample onto a photosensitive cell. Essentially, then, the baseline represents maximum light transmittance, and any deviation indicates loss, or absorbance of the light.

The spectrum is traditionally divided into several regions:

far infrared	>50,000 nm
infrared (IR)	2,500 - 50,000 nm
near infrared	800 - 2,500 nm
visible	380 - 800 nm
ultraviolet (UV)	210 - 380 nm
far ultraviolet	<210 nm

In general analytical chemistry, all three major regions (IR, visible, and UV) are utilized. However, in liquid chromatography, IR spectrophotometers have found only limited use. The reason for this is that there are few transparent polar liquids which could be used as the mobile phase. On the other hand, spectrophotometers working in the UV and part (usually up to 600 nm) of the visible range are used widely as LC detectors.

The application of ultraviolet or visible light absorption to stream monitoring is a natural extension of the use of spectrophotometers to examine individual portions of the effluent. In contrast to the refractive index, UV or visible (just as infrared) absorption is a specific parameter in that the sample material must exhibit a suitable extinction at some region of the UV spectrum or, in the case of visible absorption, combine with a complexing reagent to form a color derivative. This monitoring approach at a given wavelength is among the simplest to evaluate since the UV absorption characteristics are either known from prior work on the system, or can be easily obtained by running an absorption spectrum on a manual or recording spectrophotometer. The discovery of a suitable color-developing reagent for visible absorption requires more chemistry, but the evaluation procedure is the same.

The majority of organic compounds can be analyzed by UV-visible detectors. Many researchers feel that at least 65% of the samples analyzed by liquid chromatography can be seen to absorb some light in the 254 nm region (where most general-purpose, single-wavelength UV detectors work) and over 90% to absorb somewhere in the range of the more sophisticated variable wavelength detectors. This fact, plus the relative ease of its operation, makes the UV detector the most useful and the most widely used LC detector.

The usefulness of the LC detector is further enhanced in several of the new systems which not only monitor the column effluent at one or more wavelengths, but also allow the flow to be stopped, trapping the isolated component in the cell where wavelength changes can be carried out in such a manner as to provide a full spectrum or other information on the light-absorbing properties of the compound.

The importance of spectroscopic measurements to the successful practice of liquid chromatography cannot be overstated. The combination of these two techniques, i.e., separation and spectroscopy, produces results which neither technique can provide alone: liquid chromatography provides the separation of a complex sample matrix, and spectroscopy provides both confirmation that chromatography is complete and positive identification of the separated compounds.

Below, information related mainly to the use of UV spectroscopy as means of detection is discussed. For more detailed information on various aspects, the following literature should be consulted:

R.W. Yost, J. Stoveken and W. MacLean,
Positive Peak Identification in Liquid
Chromatography Using Absorbance Ratioing
With a Variable Wavelength Spectrophoto-
metric Detector.
Journal of Chromatography 134, 73-82 (1977).

R.W. Yost, J.M. Attebery, A.F. Poile, and
R.D. Conlon, Separation and Spectroscopy;
Rapid Isolation and Identification Via HPLC.
Perkin-Elmer Technical Note TN-66, (1978).

L.S. Ettre, Selective Detection in Column
Chromatography.
Journal of Chromatographic Science 16,
396-417 (1978).

A.F. Poile and R.D. Conlon, Spectroscopic
Solutions to LC Separation Problems.
Perkin-Elmer Technical Note TN-78, (1979).

4.442 BASIC TERMS

A few spectroscopic terms are commonly used to
characterize the response of the UV detectors and
the compounds analyzed by them.

Absorbance. Absorbance of a substance is the
logarithm of the ratio of the intensities of the
incident light (I_0) and the transmitted light (I).
It is related according to the Beer-Lambert Law
to the molar absorptivity (molar extinction coefficient, ε), the thickness of the substance (i.e.,
the path length of the cell, L) and the molar
concentration of the substance (c):

$$A = \log \frac{I_0}{I} = \varepsilon Lc \qquad (19)$$

In LC, just as in most spectrophotometers, the
electronic design of the amplifier compensates for
the logarithmic relationship making the detector
response linearly related to concentration.

AUFS. In chromatography, the ordinate of the
chromatogram represents the quantitative signal:
the more sample present, the larger the peak
height. Since chromatographic systems permit the
quantitative analysis of sample components repre-

Table 4-1. Molar Absorptivity (ε) Values of Various
Compound Types and Compounds at Specified Wavelengths.

COMPOUND TYPE (COMPOUND)	CHROMOPHORE	WAVELENGTH nm	ε
acetylide	$-C{\equiv}C$	175-180	6,000
aldehyde	$-CHO$	210	1,500
		280-300	11-18
amine	$-NH_2$	195	2,800
azido	${>}C{=}N-$	190	5,000
azo	$-N{=}N-$	285-400	3-25
bromide	$-Br$	208	300
carboxyl	$-COOH$	200-210	50-70
disulfide	$-S-S-$	194	5,500
		255	400
ester	$-COOR$	205	50
ether	$-O-$	185	1,000
iodide	$-I$	260	400
ketone	${>}C{=}O$	195	1,000
		270-285	15-30
nitrate	$-ONO_2$	270	12
nitrile	$-C{\equiv}N$	160	-
nitrite	$-ONO$	220-230	1000-2000
		300-400	10
nitro	$-NO_2$	210	strong
nitroso	$-N{=}O$	302	100
oxime	$-NOH$	190	5,000
sulfone	$-SO_2$	180	-
sulfoxide	${>}S{\rightarrow}O$	210	1,500
thioether	$-S-O$	194	4,600
		215	1,600
thioketone	${>}S{=}S$	205	strong
thiol	$-SH$	195	1,400
unsaturation, conjugated	$-(C{=}C)_3-$	260	35,000
	$-(C{=}C)_4-$	300	52,000
	$-(C{=}C)_5-$	330	118,000
unsaturation, aliphatic	$-C{=}C-$	190	8,000
	$-(C{=}C)_2-$	210-230	21,000
unsaturation, alicyclic	$-(C{=}C)_2-$	230-260	3000-8000
miscellaneous compounds	$C{=}C-C{\equiv}C$	291	6,500
	$C{=}C-C{=}N$	220	23,000
	$C{=}C-C{=}O$	210-250	10,000-20,000
		300-350	weak
	$C{=}C-NO_2$	229	9,500

COMPOUND TYPE (COMPOUND)	CHROMOPHORE	WAVELENGTH nm	ε
anthracene		252	199,000
		375	7,900
benzene		184	46,700
		202	6.900
		255	170
diphenyl		246	20,000
isoquinoline		218	80,000
		366	4,000
		417	3,500
naphthalene		220	112,000
		275	5,600
		312	175
pyridine		174	80,000
		195	6,000
		251	1,700
quinoline		227	37,000
		270	3,600
		314	2,750

senting many orders of magnitude - from ppm to percent concentrations - one may select, depending on the concentration level, various amplification ranges so that the visual display of components representing both small and large concentrations should be on-scale peaks. With most detectors, the expression of the amplification is simply a factor of the product of the actual peak height and this factor would give the peak height at maximum amplifier sensitivity.

In UV detection, due to the linearizing nature of the amplifier (converting a logarithmic relationship into a linear one), one is usually expressing the actual range used in a different manner by giving the absorbance corresponding at that particular setting to full-scale recorder response. This value is called the absorbance units (corresponding to) full scale or AUFS. From this value, the absorbance corresponding to an actual peak can easily be calculated. For example, if the 0.01 AUFS key is initiated, then a peak with a height representing 40% full scale corresponds to 0.004 absorbance units while at a setting of 0.04 AUFS a

peak with a height representing 25% full scale
equals 0.01 absorbance units.

Optical density (or O.D. - not to be confused with
outside diameter!) is an obsolete term. It represents the absorbance (cf. eq. 20) measured with a
1-cm cell i.e., when L=1cm. Hence, published O.D.
values can generally be assumed to indicate the
same signal intensity as absorbance values if the
absorbance measurement was performed in an instrument utilizing a cell with a 1 cm path length. If
a 6 mm cell is used, one absorbance unit is equal
to 0.6 O.D. To allow correlation of modern results
with earlier published work, it has become convenient to record detector settings in terms of
absorbance readings through a 1 centimeter cell,
and the designation "A 1 cm" is used.

Molar Absorptivity. This term (ε) - also called
the molar extinction coefficient - corresponds to
the absorbance for a molar concentration of the
substance with a path length of 1 cm. The extent
is dependent on the wavelength and functional
group relationship and, under defined conditions,
(solvent, pH and temperature) is a constant at a
specified wavelength.

Table 4-1 lists the molar absorptivities of a
number of compound types at specified wavelengths.
The knowledge of these values is important because
they indicate the wavelengths to be selected for
maximum response.

4.443 GENERAL CONSIDERATIONS

Since UV detectors respond only to those substances which absorb the UV light which is projected
through the cell, some consideration must be given
to the types of materials which can be seen by the
detectors. Substances capable of being analyzed by
UV include all those with one or more double bonds
(pi electrons) and materials having unshared, or
unbonded electrons. These include all olefins,
aromatics, and compounds containing $>C=O, >C=S$,
$-N-O, -N=N-$, etc. groups. Table 4-1 indicates
the characteristic chromophoric groups and the

wavelengths where significant absorptivity is
observed. Most compounds containing benzene rings
have absorptivities of at least 10^4. Absorptivity
increases with increasing unsaturation and conjugated compounds are especially absorptive. Thus, a
material such as a steroid having conjugated double
bonds would have a much higher absorptivity than
a steroid with a saturated skeleton.

It is, however, not enough that the sample components have suitable absorption in the detector's
range. A primary requirement for successful detection is that the mobile phase system which is
carrying the sample through the detector should not
absorb energy at the wavelength in use. This is
visualized in Figure 4-16 where the absorbance
spectra of two liquids commonly used as mobile
phase constituents and two actual sample components
are superimposed. Ideally, if detection takes place
where the compound exhibits maximum absorption,
maximum sensitivity for that compound will be
achieved. Note that if the mobile phase includes
significant amounts of chloroform, detection below
240 nm would be impossible; however, use of a
lower-absorbing eluent such as hexane allows detection at wavelengths as low as 195 nm.

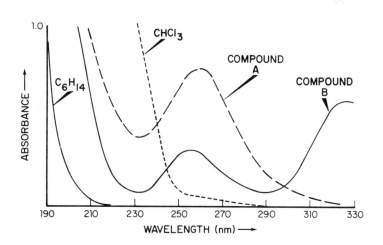

Fig. 4-16. Ultraviolet absorption of various compounds
as a function of wavelength.

Tables which can be found in the literature (as in
Table 3-3), or manufacturer's specifications,
always list the UV cutoff of a solvent i.e., the
wavelength below which it should not be used as
mobile phase constituent. This value represents
the point at which the solvent is 90% transparent.
For example, chloroform is said to be suitable
for such use at wavelengths above 245 nm. As seen
on the chloroform curve in Figure 4-16, solvents
can still interfere somewhat at wavelengths above
their rated limit. This frequently shows up as a
baseline shift when solvents or solvent ratios are
changed, even though the "chart" value (i.e., the
specified cutoff point) would indicate that there
should be no interference.

Naturally, in addition to its absorption properties, the mobile phase should not influence the
detector in other ways: for instance, the detector
should be insensitive to flow or temperature
changes, just to mention two variables. UV detectors generally fulfill these criteria; therefore,
no additional temperature control is normally
required in the usual laboratory environment and
detectors are sufficiently insensitive to changes
in the flow rates so that a simple pump or even
gravity feed can be employed in less demanding
situations.

Sample size requirement is dependent upon the
absorption characteristic of the sample used, but
an acceptable minimum sample size under average
conditions is about 1 ng of a substance.

4.444 FIXED-WAVELENGTH DETECTORS

The light source most commonly available in UV
detectors has most of its energy at a fixed wavelength of 253.7 nanometers. This is a result of
the very strong line emitted at that point by
low-pressure mercury vapor lamps. By filtering
out all other more weakly emitted wavelengths,
manufacturers have been able to utilize this 254
nm line to provide extremely stable, highly sensitive detectors capable of measuring even sub-
nanogram quantities of strongly absorbing materials. The 254 nm detector has been liquid chroma-

tography's most useful low-cost detector, since most UV absorbing compounds have some absorbance at 254 nm.

Many of the fixed wavelength detectors also offer filters which provide a limited utilization of the detector at other wavelengths for the detection of those compounds which have no absorbance at 254 nm, but have at some other wavelength. However, the baseline stability and signal strength of these weaker lines generally never equal that received at 254 nm.

4.445 VARIABLE-WAVELENGTH DETECTORS

Variable wavelength detectors are particularly useful in three cases:

- best sensitivity would be obtained at a wave-length other than 254 nm or other wavelengths for which filters are available;

- the individual sample components have high absorptivity at different wavelengths and thus, operation at a single wavelength would reduce the system's sensitivity or would even make the detection of certain sample compo-nents impossible;

- stopflow operation combined with peak scanning is desired.

An example of each is shown here to illustrate the first two points; stopflow operation will be dis-cussed separately.

Investigation of Table 4-1 shows that there are a number of compounds which have particularly strong absorbance in the border region between UV and far UV (190-210 nm). Thus, the possibility of operatin here is particularly useful. Most variable wave-length detectors permit this. A practical example, the analysis of vitamins, is shown in Figure 4-17. If only thiamine or pyridoxine were present, one may work at 254 or 324 nm, but at these wavelengths, some of the other vitamins have no response. How-ever, at 200 nm, all five vitamins show high absorptivity.

The second practical example illustrates the use of two different wavelengths within a single run. The chromatogram is shown in Figure 4-18. Here, a contraceptive pill is analyzed for two steroids. Both steroids have absorption at 227 nm; however, at this wavelength another component, which is also

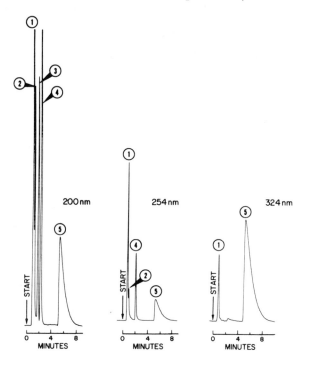

Fig. 4-17. Analysis of vitamins at different wavelengths with an UV detector.
Column: 50 cm x 2.6 mm I.D., packed with ODS-Sil-X-I particles: 37 μm, fully porous. Mobile phase: water, 2 mL/min. Column temperature: 65°C. Peaks: 1 thiamine, 2 ascorbic acid, 3 panthenol, 4 niacin, 5 pyrodoxine.

present in the matrix, would interfere with the estrogenic steroid making its determination impossible. On the other hand, at 283 nm, where this steroid has good absorptivity and there is no interference, the androgenic steroid has no response. Therefore, the best way to perform routine analysis is to change the wavelength during a run.

Figure 4-19 shows the optical schematic of a UV detector with variable-wavelength capability. Modern UV detectors are capable of operation at any selected wavelength between 190 and 600 nm.

Depending on the sophistication of the detector, wavelength change is done manually or programmed on a time basis into the memory of the system, allowing unattended operation. Sophisticated systems also permit automatic scanning in the full

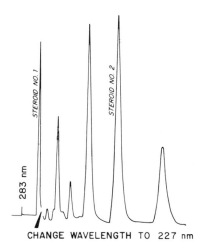

Fig. 4-18. *Analysis of a contraceptive pill for steroids, utilizing variable wavelength UV detection. Column: 50 cm x 2.6 mm I.D., packed with ODS-Sil-X-I; particles: 37 μm, fully porous. Mobile phase: 94: 6 methanol-water, 1 mL/min. Column temperature: 25°C. Steroids: 1 estrogenic, 2 androgenic.*

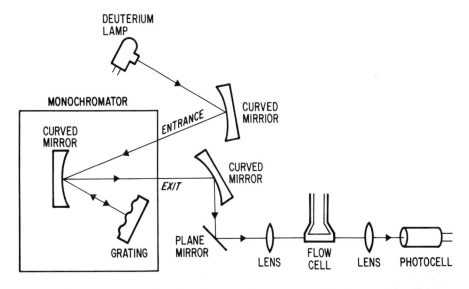

Fig. 4-19. *Optical schematic of a typical UV liquid chromatography detector.*

wavelength range while the flow is stopped and a given fraction of the column effluent is held in the cell.

The heart of an efficient UV detector is the cell. Figure 4-20 shows the schematic of a modern flow-through cell, offered by Perkin-Elmer, indicating its position directly in the light path of the detector. The optics provide focusing of the light beam in the center of the cell where it is virtu-ally unaffected by the entry-exit-window-interface disturbance, or drift induced by flow, temperature, or refractive index changes. The short, wide cell assures that maximum energy is transmitted, and a post-cell collecting lens focuses all of the exist-ing light from the cell onto the photodetector. Since the high performance of the detector is to a large degree achieved through the use of a flow-cell which is less than one centimeter long, the output signal is amplified to give response equal to that which would be received if a 1 cm path-length had been used.

4.446 STOPFLOW OPERATION

As already mentioned, a special feature of some variable wavelength UV detectors is the ability to perform spectroscopic scanning and precise absorb-ance readings at a variety of wavelengths while the peak is at rest in a flowcell. Stopflow spectroscopy adds a new dimension of analytical capability to liquid chromatography because it permits qualitative information to be obtained beyond simple identification by retention time.

There are two major applications of stopflow chromatography. In the first, one can evaluate the best wavelength(s) to be selected for actual anal-ysis. This is particularly important when no infor-mation is available on molar absorptivities at different wavelengths. The following example will illustrate this application; it is related to the analysis of an orange oil sample.

It is known that limonene represents about 98% of this oil and that limonene has an absorption maxi-mum at 220 nm. There was, however, no information

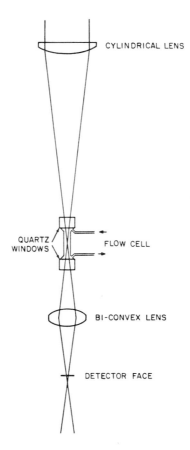

CYLINDRICAL LENS

QUARTZ
WINDOWS

FLOW CELL

BI-CONVEX LENS

DETECTOR FACE

Fig. 4-20. Flowcell for variable wavelength UV detectors and its position in the light path.

available on the absorptivity of the other components present at small concentration and the
primary analytical problem required analysis of
these components. Thus, the orange oil sample was
analyzed on a C_8 bonded-phase column using 99:1
acetonitrile-water as the mobile phase. Under these
conditions, the whole sample will elute unretained
from the column. The flow was stopped when the
sample was present in the detector cell and scanned
from 200 to 400 nm. Figure 4-21 shows the scan
obtained. Evaluation of this result shows that the
best wavelength to analyze the low concentration
components is 320 nm; at this wavelength, limonene
has no response.

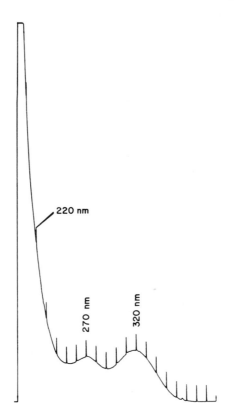

Fig. 4-21. *Stopflow scanning of column effluent in the UV detector cell from 200 to 400 nm. Sample: orange oil. Column: 25 cm x 4.6 mm I.D.; packed with RP-8 C$_8$ bonded phase; particles 10 μm, fully porous. Mobile phase: 99:1 acetonitrile-water.*

The second major application is related to the problem of peak purity: often, the peak shape in itself does not reveal that it actually corresponds to two (or even more) components. In such a case, absorbance ratioing at several wavelengths is particularly helpful in deciding whether the peak represents a single compound or, is in fact, a composite peak.

In absorbance ratioing, the absorbance is measured at two or more wavelengths and ratios are calculated for two selected wavelengths. This can be done in two ways: either at several points along the peak, e.g., the leading edge, the maximum and the trailing edge, or only at one position, e.g., the maximum. Momentary stop of the flow permits the rapid measurement at several wavelengths. Evaluation can be carried out in two ways:

In the first case, the ratios measured at different positions are compared: if they agree, the compound under the peak is pure, otherwise, the peak represents a composite of two or more peaks. In the second case, the measurements are repeated, but in this instance, during the analysis of pure substances. These ratios are then compared. If they agree, the sample component corresponding to that particular peak and the standard, are the same. If not, then there may be additional compounds under the peak, or it may even represent an entirely different substance.

Figure 4-22 and Table 4-2 represent an illustration for the second application. A urine sample was analyzed for drugs of abuse. The chromatogram, itself, was obtained at 210 nm, while absorbances were measured for the methadone and morphine peaks (at maximum) at several wavelengths. Table 4-2 lists the absorbance ratios obtained for both the actual urine sample and for separately analyzed standards. These data confirm the identification and purity of methadone, but indicate that the peak eluting with the proper retention time for morphine is not due entirely to that drug.

Table 4-2.   Absorbance Ratios for Drugs in Urine vs. Values Obtained for Pure Substances.*

DRUGS	ABSORBANCE RATIO		
	205/210	220/210	225/210
Methadone standard	1.32	0.49	0.31
Methadone in urine	1.32	0.49	0.30
Morphine standard	0.90	0.75	0.42
Morphine in urine	0.94	0.67	0.53

* For the chromatogram, see Figure 4-22.

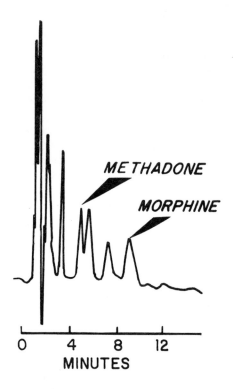

Fig. 4-22. Determination of methadone and morphine in urine utilizing absorbance ratio measurements. Column: 50 cm x 2.6 mm I.D., packed with fluoroether Sil-X-I bonded phase; particles: 37 μm, fully porous. Mobile phase: 92:8 acetonitrile-water containing 0.3% H_3PO_4; 2 mL/min. Column temperature: 70°C. UV detector at 210 nm (0.1 AUFS).

4.45 FLUORESCENCE DETECTORS

4.451 PRINCIPLES

Fluorescence detectors represent the third most commonly used detector-type in modern HPLC. For those compounds having natural fluorescing capability, or which can be made to fluoresce through derivatization, this type of detection is by far the most sensitive. Typically, fluorescence sensitivity is 1000 times higher than that of the UV detector for strong UV absorbing materials and the UV, of course, is 1000 times more sensitive than the refractive index detector. Each time the sensitivity is increased, specificity is also increased. Fluorescence detectors are the most specific and selective of all optical detectors. This is normally used as an advantage in the measurement of specific fluorescent species in samples. In fact, one of the largest potential advantages of fluorescence detection - particularly using such instrumentation which permits carrying out both excitation and emission scanning - lies in the ability to provide peak identification data through excitation and emission spectra, using stopflow scanning techniques. A great deal of information resides in the excitation and emission spectra of a compound and with more sophisticated instrumentation allowing for corrected spectra, possibilities such as computer assisted structural interpretation of fluorescence spectra exist to aid in compound identification.

Fluorescence occurs when compounds having specific functional groups are excited by shorter wavelength energy and emit higher wavelength radiation. Normally, the emission is measured at right angles to the excitation and, naturally, the actual fluorescing capacity of specific chemical groups is a function of the wavelengths of the excitation and emission.

Below, we shall deal only with some basic information related to fluorescence detectors and their use in liquid chromatography. For more detailed information, readers are referred to the textbooks on fluorescence spectrophotometry and to a few Perkin-Elmer publications listed below:

Anon.,Detection in LC - An Introduction to Fluorescence Spectroscopy. Technical Note TN-60. (1977).

J.L. DiCesare, Utilization of Fluorescence Detection Coupled to Liquid Chromatography. Technical Note FL-49.

T.J. Porro, The Technique of Liquid Chromatography With Fluorescence Detection. Trends in Fluorescence 1 (1), 7 (1978).

T.J. Porro, R.D. Conlon and J.L. DiCesare, Influence of Flowcell Characteristics on

Liquid Chromatographic Resolution and
Fluorescence Sensitivity. Technical Note
FL-64.

4.452 NATURALLY OCCURRING FLUORESCENT COMPOUNDS

There are a number of compounds which have a natural fluorescence. The most intense fluorescent
activity is found in those compounds having
aromatic functional groups with low energy $\pi \longrightarrow \pi^*$
transitions. Also, aliphatic and alicyclic com-
pounds with carbonyl groups and compounds with
highly conjugated double bonds fluoresce, but to a
lesser degree. Most unsubstituted aromatic hydrocarbons fluoresce when in solution with quantum
efficiency (intensity) increasing with the number
of rings, their degree of condensation and their
structural rigidity.

Table 4-3 summarizes information on the fluorescence of substituted benzene derivatives.

The degree of dissociation of acidic and basic
compounds dramatically affects fluorescence. This
can be seen when comparing the intensity of phenol
and aniline with their ionized forms (see Table
4-3): in case of phenol, the ionized form has
about half the intensity of the undissociated
compound, but at quite different wavelengths, while
in the case of aniline, the ionized form has no
fluorescence at all. Thus, close control of pH is
normally required in the fluorescence analysis of
ionizable materials.

Due to the specificity of the excitation and emission wavelengths, through their change, the response
to some compounds can be enhanced while others are
suppressed. For example, Figure 4-23 shows the
chromatograms obtained by analyzing the three-
component mixture of perylene, pyrene, and coronene.

By changing the emission wavelength from 395 to
450 nm, coronene is made to show considerable
emission while, at the same time, the signal for
pyrene is considerably reduced. On the other
hand, by increasing the excitation wavelength
from 338 to 368 nm, signals for pyrene and

Table 4-3. Fluorescence of Substituted Benzenes.

COMPOUND	STRUCTURE	WAVELENGTH (nm)		RELATIVE INTENSITY*
		EXCITATION	EMISSION	
Benzene	C_6H_6	270	310	10
Toluene	$C_6H_5-CH_3$	270	320	17
Propylbenzene	$C_6H_5-C_3H_7$	270	320	17
Fluorobenzene	C_6H_5-F	270	320	10
Chlorobenzene	C_6H_5-Cl	275	345	7
Bromobenzene	C_6H_5-Br	290	380	5
Iodobenzene	C_6H_5-I	-	-	0
Phenol	C_6H_5-OH	285	365	18
Phenolate ion	$C_6H_5-O^-$	310	400	10
Anisole	$C_6H_5-OCH_3$	285	345	20
Aniline	$C_6H_5-NH_2$	210	405	20
Anilinium ion	$C_6H_5-NH_3^+$	-	-	0
Benzoic acid	C_6H_5-COOH	310	390	3
Benzonitrile	C_6H_5-CN	280	360	20
Nitrobenzene	$C_6H_5-NO_2$	-	-	0

*Relative to benzene (=10).

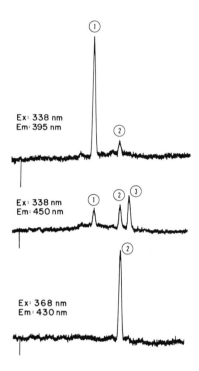

Fig. 4-23. *Selectivity of fluorescence detection for polynuclear aromatics. Column: 25 cm x 2.6 mm I.D., packed with ODS-Sil-X-I; particles: 37 µm, fully porous. Mobile phase: gradient starting at 45:55 acetonitrile-water and programmed with a linear rate of 0.45%/min to 100% water; 1 mL/min. Fluorescence detection; wavelengths listed in the chromatogram (ex=excitation, em-emission). Peaks (amount present): 1 pyrene (876 pg), 2 benzoperylene (464 pg), 3 coronene (528 pg).*

coronene are suppressed while the signal for perylene is enhanced.

If one is interested in every component present in a complex sample, then the wavelengths are usually selected as the best fit for groups of components. For example, in the very important polynuclear aromatic chromatogram, shown in Figure 4-24, the excitation and emission wavelengths were 280 and 340 nm, respectively, for the first 17 minutes of the run, and then changed to the respective values of 305 and 430 nm; the latter values represent the best compromise to allow sensitive detection of compounds 7-22.

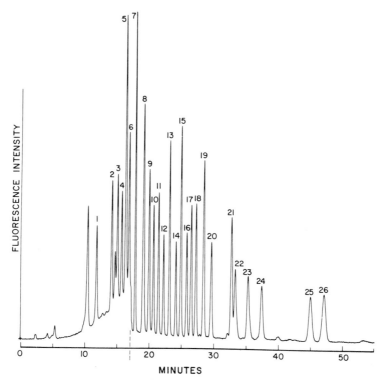

Fig. 4-24. *Analysis of polynuclear aromatics by reversed-phase liquid chromatography.*
Column: 25 cm x 2.6 mm I.D., packed with HC-ODS, particles: 10 μm, fully porous. Mobile phase: gradient elution, starting with 40:60 acetonitrile-water and programmed with a linear rate of 4%/min to 100% acetonitrile; 0.5 mL/min. Room temperature. Fluorescence detection. Wavelengths: excitation 280 nm, emission 340 nm, then changed at the broken vertical line to 305 and 430 nm respectively. Peaks: 1 *naphthalene,* 2 *1-methylnaphthalene,* 3 *acenaphthene,* 4 *fluorene,* 5 1,4-dimethylnaphthalene, 6 *phenanthrene,* 7 *anthracene,* 8 *fluoranthene,* 9 *pyrene,* 10 *8,10-dimethylanthracene,* 11 *2-methylanthracene,* 12 *benzo[a]anthracene,* 14 *chrysene,* 15 *7,12-dimethylbenz[a]anthracene,* 16 *benzo-[e]pyrene,* 17 *benzo[b]fluoranthene,* 18 *dibenz[a,c]anthracene,* 19 *benzo[k]fluoranthene,* 20 *benzo[a]pyrene,* 21 *dibenz[a,h]anthracene,* 22 *benzo[g,h,i]perylene,* 23 *indeno[1,2,3-cd]pyrene,* 24 *dibenzo[a,e]pyrene,* 25 *picene,* 26 *p-quaterphenyl.*

Polynuclear aromatics probably represent the most important sample type with natural fluorescence. Besides these, a number of other compounds of primary interest in food technology, pharmacology, and clinical medicine also have natural fluorescence detection and, therefore, fluorescence detection is highly recommended for their analysis.

4.453 FLUORESCENT DERIVATIVES

Quite often, highly fluorescing derivatives of various chemical eluent compounds can be formed, either prior to chromatography or in the post-column eluent to convert nonfluorescing species into highly fluorescing ones. Derivatives are generally referred to as substances formed from the parent compound by the modification of only one atom or a proton. These fluorescence derivatives generally result in marked improvement in sensitivity. Several types of derivatives have been used successfully: Figure 4-25 shows the

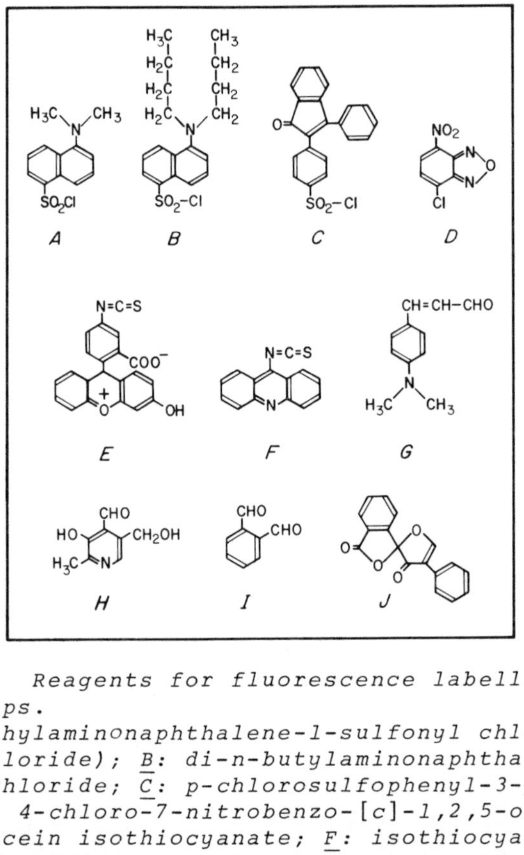

Fig. 4-25. Reagents for fluorescence labelling of amino groups.
A: 5-dimethylaminonaphthalene-1-sulfonyl chloride (dansyl chloride); B: di-n-butylaminonaphthalene-1-sulfonyl chloride; C: p-chlorosulfophenyl-3-phenyl indone; D: 4-chloro-7-nitrobenzo-[c]-1,2,5-oxadiazole; E: fluorescein isothiocyanate; F: isothiocyanatoacridine; G: p-dimethylamino-cinnamaldehyde; H: pyridoxal; I: o-phthaldialdehyde; J: fluorescamine.

formulae of the most widely used derivative
forming reagents while Figure 4-26 gives the reaction of the two most widely used reagents with
amino acids. Probably amino acid and amine analysis is the field where the use of liquid chromatography with fluorescence detection is the most
widespread. Figure 4-27 shows a chromatogram of
polyamines analyzed as dansyl derivatives by
reversed-phase liquid chromatography with fluorescence detection.

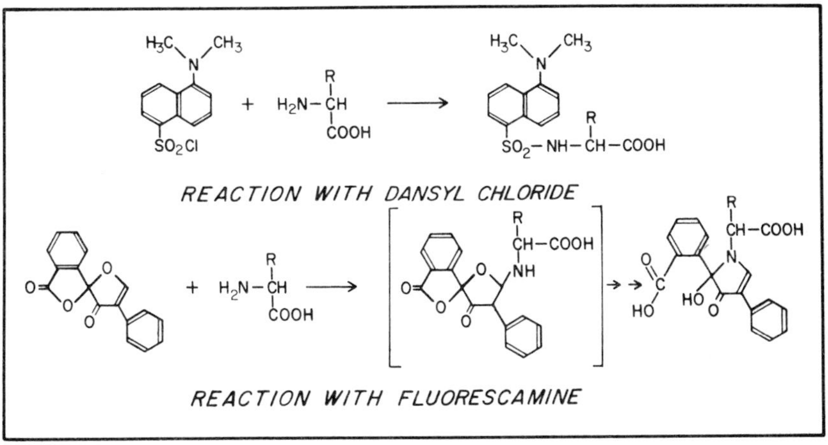

Fig. 4-26. Reaction of α-amino acids with dansyl chloride
and fluorescamine.

The liquid chromatographic conditions, particularly
the selection of the mobile phase, have strong
influence on the fluorescence characteristics of
the derivatives. For example, in case of dansyl
derivatives, the fluorescence efficiency* increases
and the maximum emission wavelength decreases with
decreasing dielectric constant. As an example,
Table 4-4 lists data for dansyl tryptophan.

The following two books discuss derivative forming
and their use in liquid chromatography in detail:

J.F. Lawrence and R.W. Frei, Chemical
Derivatization in Liquid Chromatography.
Elsevier, Amsterdam, Oxford, New York, 1976.

*Fluorescence efficiency or quantum efficiency is
the ratio of the quanta emitted to the quanta
absorbed. It never exceeds unity.

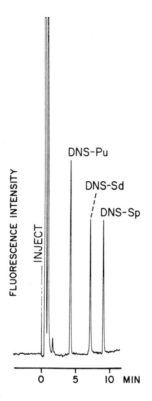

Fig. 4-27. Analysis of polyamines by reversed-phase liquid chromatography. Column: 25 cm x 2.6 mm I.D., packed with HC-ODS bonded phase; particles: 10 μm, fully porous. Mobile phase: gradient, starting at 51:49 methanol-water and programmed with a linear rate of 3.5%/min to 85:15 methanol-water; 2 mL/min. Column temperature: 60°C. Fluorescence detection. Wavelengths: excitation 340 nm, emission 515 nm. Peaks: dansyl (DNS) derivatives of putresceine (Pu), spermidine (Sd) and spermine (Sp).

K. Blau and G.S. King, Handbook of Derivatives for Chromatography.
Heyden, London, Bellmawr, Rheine, 1977.

4.454 FLUORESCENCE DETECTORS

Figure 4-28 shows the optical schematic of a typical fluorescence detector for liquid chromatography. The commercially available detectors differ in the manner in which the wavelengths are controlled. Less expensive instruments utilize filters; medium priced units offer monochromator control of

Table 4-4. Fluorescence Efficiency and Emission
Maximum of Dansyl-D,L-Tryptophan in Solvents of
Different Dielectric Constants.

MOBILE PHASE	SOLVENT DIELECTRIC CONSTANT debye	EMISSION MAXIMUM nm	FLUORESCENCE EFFICIENCY
Water	78.5	578	0.068
Glycerol	42.5	553	0.18
Ethylene glycol	37.0	543	0.36
Proplene glycol	32.0	538	0.37
Dimethylformamide	36.5	517	0.59
Ethanol	25.8	529	0.50
n-Butanol	19.2	519	0.50
Acetone	21.5	513	0.35
Ethyl acetate	6.1	510	0.54
Chloroform	5.1	508	0.41
Dioxane	3.0	500	0.70

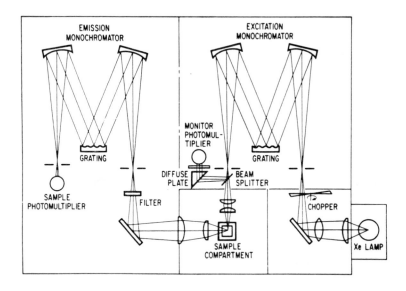

Fig. 4-28. Optical schematic of a typical fluorescence
detector for liquid chromatography.

at least one function, usually excitation wavelength, and full capability research-grade instruments provide monochromator control of both excitation and emission wavelengths.

4.46 ELECTROCHEMICAL DETECTORS

4.461 PRINCIPLES

The electrochemical (or polarographic) detector is
the next logical step in liquid chromatography
detection. Although it is not yet widely used
because of operational difficulties, it must be
considered by the chromatographer because of the
additional selectivity and sensitivity for some
compounds.

This detector is based on the oxidation or reduc-
of the eluting compound at a suitable electrode
and the measurement of the resulting current. The
detection principle is based on the familiar
dropping mercury polarograph where an oxidation
or reduction (halfwave) potential is imposed on an
electrode pair sufficient to produce a diffusion
current. Since the current level is a direct
measure of concentration, the process is a quantitative one.

To apply this technique to liquid chromatography
detection, new electrode materials have been
developed and efficient low-volume cell geometries
have been designed. Carbon paste, glossy carbon
and gold-mercury amalgam are used, often with a
silver-silver chloride counter-electrode.

The area of application of electrochemical detection is not as large as RI, UV or fluorescence,
but the compounds for which it does apply,
represent some of the most important drug, pollut-
ant and natural product classes of compounds. For
these, the specificity, and 50 to 100 times increase in sensitivity make it very useful for
monitoring these compounds in complex matrices
such as body fluids and natural products. Sensitivities for compounds such as phenol, catechol-
amines, nitrosamines, and organic acids are in the
picomole (nanogram) range.

4.462 GENERAL CONSIDERATIONS

Some important considerations and limitations of electrochemical detection are:

The mobile phase must be made electrically conductive, usually by the addition of a suitable salt. This limits or prohibits the use of most normal phase separations using hexane or other nonpolar mobile phases. Ion-exchange and reversed-phase chromatography represent a rich area of application. However, one must realize that the addition of salts to the mobile phase may change the chromatography.

Another requirement concerning the mobile phase is that it must be purged of oxygen, metal contaminants and halides in order to reduce the background current and therefore, noise and drift in the baseline.

Concerning the samples, the components to be detected must be oxidizable or reducible at a potential which does not also electrolyze the mobile phase or sample background compounds.

4.47 MISCELLANEOUS DETECTORS

Several other detectors are also available. None have found much general use, since each has several drawbacks which make their utilization difficult or extremely limited.

4.471 FLAME IONIZATION DETECTOR

The flame ionization detector has long served gas chromatography, and the mechanics of thermal ionization and ion-current monitoring are well known and demonstrated. The effluent-stream sampling problem, however, is made more complex in liquid chromatography because the mobile phase must be separated from the sample before it enters the detector. To do this, some means must be provided for carrying the eluent stream through a vaporization process, normally a combination of heat and vacuum, before it reaches the primary ionization cell. At least three mechanisms have been

used to get the sample into the flame cone including:

- burning residue directly on the wire;

- using the heat of the flame to volatilize the
sample before ignition; and

- providing a heated chamber between the wire
and the burner where the sample is removed
from the wire by pyrolysis and the gaseous
pyrolysis products directed into the flame.

The use of a flame ionization detector for LC
detection has one primary advantage: it is a
"general" detector which can be used with gradient
elution techniques. However, it has a number of
shortcomings such as loss of sample in the evap-
oration chamber; high baseline noise level resulting from wire or moving belt contamination; low
limits of detection, no better than that achieved
with RI detectors; and a high degree of complexity
in establishing optimum operating parameters. For
these reasons, the detector has had only limited
use and only for high-boiling compounds, such as
lipids, proteinaceous materials and polymers.

4.472 ELECTROLYTIC CONDUCTIVITY DETECTOR

In electrolytic conductivity detectors, the
specific conductivity of the effluent stream is
continuously measured and an entrained sample is
indicated by a change in conductivity.

To utilize this technique for stream monitoring,
the immersion cell is replaced by a low-volume
flowthrough cell and variations in conductivity
of the mobile phase due to the eluted sample
components are continously recorded. Response
is linear with concentration over a wide range,
so quantitation of the output signal is possible
with suitable preliminary calibration. Best use
is made of this detector in isocratic analysis
since solvent gradients will cause a proportional
shift in the baseline.

One of the basic shortcomings of electrolytic
conductivity detectors is cell instability. Such

detectors have been used most successfully in
ion-exchange chromatography of anions and cations,
but generally, they have found only limited
popular acceptance.

4.473 HEAT OF ADSORPTION DETECTOR

The heat-of-adsorption detector is considered to
be an universal detector. It is based on the
detection of the minute temperature changes which
accompany the interaction of sample and mobile
phase with the separation medium in the column.
As solvent molecules are displaced by sample
molecules at the adsorbent surface, a local temperature change reflects the exchange. A thermistor is used to detect the temperature change of
the adsorbent and a second thermistor imbedded in
a nonadsorbing granular material is provided to
aid in compensating for changes in stream or
ambient temperature.

Many approaches have been used in measuring these
thermal reactions, including imbedding thermistors
in the column, temperature monitoring at the point
of emergence of the effluent from the column bed,
and directing the effluent through a cell containing a small portion of the column bed material
and the measuring thermistor. The latter approach
is favored because of the flexibility offered. By
repacking the cell or substituting a second prepacked cell, the unit can be moved from column-to-
column for a variety of studies.

In actual practice, the difficulty of maintaining
temperature equilibria and interpreting the often
confusing above-and-below-the-baseline peaks in
addition to the need for repacking the cell each
time column changes are made, have made this a
very little used detector.

4.48 DUAL DETECTOR SYSTEMS

In many cases, the use of a single detection might
give ambiguous or even incorrect results. This is
particularly true for complex, natural samples.
For this reason, the simultaneous use of two
detectors is often preferred.

There are three reasons for dual detector operation. In the first case, by combining a RI and an UV detector, one can achieve an almost universal detecting capacity. In the second case, a selective detector is combined with a general purpose detector; by this combination, one can obtain the general "fingerprint"-type chromatogram of the sample and, at the same time, identify certain peaks. Finally, in the third case, one may combine two UV detectors operated at two different wavelengths, e.g., by combining a fixed-wavelength and a variable wavelength detector.

In gas chromatography where the most frequently used ionization detectors destroy the sample, dual-detector systems split the column effluent and the two detectors are parallel to each other. This is, however, not necessary in liquid chromatography since none of the common detectors are destructive as far as the sample is concerned. Thus, the two detectors can be connected in series. If both detectors employ good design principles, i.e., have no peak-broadening, it is generally not critical as to which unit is placed first in the series. If any doubt exists, it is possible to run the same analysis through each while it is connected separately and place the detector which exhibits the narrowest peak first, in the stream.

In dual detector systems, it is convenient to fit the instrument with a second injector and column permitting use of either one column with two detectors in series, or two columns each with a separate detector as separate LC systems. Naturally, one needs dual pumps for this purpose. In this way, the system may be used as two separate chromatographs when sample load is high. The only restriction for such application is that only isocratic analyses can be performed in the parallel mode.

Part Five:
Qualitative Analysis

The purpose of most chromatographic investigations is to <u>analyze</u> the sample. Determining what, or how many <u>components</u> are in the sample is referred to as <u>qualitative</u> analysis; while determining the <u>amount of some</u>, or all, of the components present is referred to as <u>quantitative</u> analysis.

Chromatography is essentially a separation technique and, as such, about the best presently available. However, it is a "blind" method. It indicates the presence of a substance without telling what it is, and it results in a signal which can be related to the amount present without actually revealing the identity. Therefore, the methods of interpreting the chromatograms are of vital interest to the practical chromatographer.

Here we can only discuss briefly the various techniques and we cannot go into too much detail. Readers who are interested in more information are referred to the various chapters of the general textbooks and monographs dealing with liquid chromatography. This part concerns qualitative analysis while questions associated with quantitative analysis are subject of the next part.

5.1 USE OF RETENTION DATA

Since, under given conditions, the retention time of a certain substance on a given column is characteristic of the particular substance, retention data can be used for identification purposes. In doing this, however, a number of questions have to be taken into consideration.

First, it should be understood that the reproducibility of <u>absolute</u> retention data depends on a number of <u>instrumental</u> conditions. The <u>retention time</u> (t_R) and the <u>adjusted retention time</u> (t_R') are commonly used for identification purposes (see Figure 2-1):

Retention time (t_R) - the time (or distance) elapsed between the point of injection and the maximum of the peak.

Observed retention time of an unretained compound (t_M) - the time (distance) from start to the maximum of the peak of an unretained material, frequently benzene.

Adjusted retention time (t_R') - the time (distance) from the maximum of the peak corresponding to the unretained solute to the maximum of the peak of interest:

$$t_R' = t_R - t_M \tag{20}$$

Multiplied by the flowrate (F_c), the corresponding retention volumes are obtained:

Retention volume, $V_R = t_R F_c$

Adjusted retention volume, $V_R' = t_R' F_c$

Volume of mobile phase in the column (+ system), also called the void volume or interstitial volume, $V_M = t_M F_c$

In the literature, one may sometimes find the expression net retention volume (V_N) instead of the adjusted retention volume. In gas chromatography, the two terms are different: The net retention volume is equal to the adjusted retention volume multiplied by the compressibility correction factor. Since, in liquid chromatography, mobile phase compressibility can be neglected, here the two terms have the same meaning.

The best practical way for expressing retention data is to give the relative retention (r), i.e., the retention expressed relative to the retention of a standard. The relative retention is expressed as:

$$r_{i,st} = \frac{t_R'(i)}{t_R'(st)} = \frac{V_R'(i)}{V_R'(st)} = \frac{k_i}{k_{st}} \tag{21}$$

where subscripts i and st refer to the respective values for the individual peak and the peak of the standard. The symbol k refers to the <u>capacity</u> <u>factor</u> (<u>capacity ratio</u>) discussed in <u>detail</u> in Chapter 2.

In Chapter 2, we have already dealt in detail with the relative retention also called the <u>separation</u> <u>factor</u>. Here, a few additional considerations are <u>listed</u> which are necessary if meaningful relative retention values are to be determined and utilized:

- If possible, the standard should be part of the sample actually analyzed. If it is not present in the original sample, it should be mixed with it prior to chromatographic analysis.

- The standard should be selected so that it will fall near the middle of the series of substances whose relative retentions are to be determined.

- The smallest possible sample sizes should be used because the sample size may influence the retention time.

When applying retention data, one should not forget that these data are characteristic, but not specific. This means that more than one substance may have the same retention value. There is less possibility of error if retention data on two different columns (one polar and one non-polar, or two having different activities) are determined and used for peak identification.

5.2 ADDITION OF THE SUPPOSED COMPONENT TO THE SAMPLE

Naturally, the easiest method for comparing retention times is to mix a portion of the sample successively with the pure substances which are supposed to be its components, and to compare the chromatograms obtained by analyzing the original sample and the mixture of the sample plus pure substance. If the substance which was added was already present in the original sample, one of the peaks will be relatively larger than in the original chromatogram.

The trouble with this method is that it only shows
that the added pure substance and the sample component corresponding to the particular peak have
identical (or very close) retention times; however, it does not give an absolute proof for the
identity of the two substances. Therefore, repetition of the method on another column with different polarity is always recommended; overlapping on
both columns represents a far more convincing
proof than on only one column.

While the technique of adding the supposed component to the sample does not represent an absolute
proof in the identification of a particular component, it is an absolute proof if used in the
negative sense, that is, for the exclusion of the
possibility of the presence of a particular substance. In this case, the chromatogram of the
mixture of the original sample and the added
standard will show an additional peak not present
in the original chromatogram. A second case, when
this technique is particularly recommended, is if
the composition of the sample is known, but one is
still not sure as to the assignment of the individual peaks to the respective components.

It is extremely important that before mixing it
with the sample, the purity of the "pure" substances to be added be checked by chromatographic
analysis on the same column and under identical
conditions in order to prevent any misinterpretation due to peaks of impurities in the allegedly
pure standards.

5.3 RETENTION PLOTS

The retention values of substances belonging to
certain homologous series can usually be related
to various physical characteristics of the substances or to their structure. In a large number
of cases, these (usually semilog) plots show a
linear relationship while early members of the
homologous series might deviate somewhat from it.
The importance of such plots is that if the identity of certain peaks in a multicomponent mixture
is known, other peaks belonging to the same homologous series may be readily identified, or if

retention values of only some member of a homologous series are known, values for the other
members can be obtained by interpolation or
extrapolation.

For such plots, the adjusted retention times (t_R')
and volumes (V_R'), or the relative retention $(\underline{r})$
data are used. The most frequently utilized plots
relate the log of the retention data to the number
of carbon atoms.

5.4 PEAK SHIFTING TECHNIQUE

Retention values generally change with the mobile
phase and its composition. In many cases, this
change will not be identical for every substance,
and the relative position of individual peaks in
a complex mixture will differ somewhat if the
same sample is analyzed under different conditions;
some peaks will move closer to each other while
others will move further apart. Such relative peak
shifting can particularly be observed if the
sample consists of components of quite different
polarity. In such cases, even the order of elution of certain peaks may be reversed if the analytical conditions are changed.

5.5 POST-COLUMN QUALITATION TECHNIQUES

A major advantage of liquid chromatography is that
the separated peak is easy to recover for further
qualitative analyses. It is always present in the
solvent stream which has passed through the detector and may be readily collected at the detector
exit line for further chemical or spectroscopic
analysis. Examples of the infrared analyses of LC
fractions is described in great detail in the
following Perkin-Elmer report:

> Identification of LC Fractions by Infrared
> Spectroscopy. LC Applications Study No. 61,
> Perkin-Elmer, Norwalk, (1977).

Figure 5-1 visualizes the sample handling steps
for the direct infrared analysis of LC effluent
fractions.

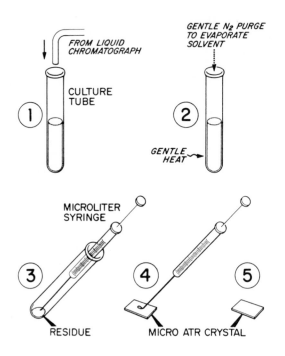

Fig. 5-1. Sample handing steps for the direct infrared analysis of a liquid chromatographic fraction.

Several LC detectors allow the eluent to be held
in the cell with the flow stopped; this is possible
because liquids diffuse at such low rates that
practically no sample movement occurs when there is
no flow. Then the characteristics of the light beam
are modified to yield spectral information about
the component (or components) which have been isolated in the cell, either by manual adjustments in
wavelength or by mechanized scanning of the wavelength selector(s). Normal fluorescence and/or UV
spectra may be obtained in this way, or absorbance
readings can be compared with those of standards
to achieve compound identification. With the help
of sophisticated detector systems, it is also
possible to obtain rapid, accurate, qualitative
spectral and absorbance ratio information on components which have been isolated in the detector
flowcell. All these techniques are discussed in
detail in a previous part of this book.

5.6 AVAILABILITY OF RETENTION DATA

Retention data can be found in some liquid chromatography publications. Some papers on the application of chromatography tabulate retention data. Thus, one must check the bibliography of his particular subject to find out what data is available. Theoretically, if analyzed under identical conditions, retention data should be reproducible from laboratory-to-laboratory. The problem, however, is that often the conditions are different even if not specifically stated. The fact that the mobile phase systems are different can usually be seen from the publications, however, it is often not evident that the columns are dissimilar even if they are identically described. The reason for this is that columns available from different sources have different activity levels. Therefore, there is little hope in LC to be able to reproduce exactly published retention data. However, these data are still useful because one can usually rely on the retention order obtained in a particular elution system.

5.7 ARTIFACTS

In chromatographic analysis, the natural purpose is always to determine the composition of the original sample, and one assumes that the peaks which appear on the chromatogram refer to the individual constituents of his sample. However, this is not always true and sometimes artifact peaks not related to the original sample might also appear in the chromatogram.

There are several main sources from which such artifact peaks may originate.

A primary source for artifact peaks is material from previous samples which was adsorbed (retained) on the column or the injection system. Many samples contain, in trace quantities, impurities which the analyst is unaware of. Since these usually have retention times much longer than the expected analysis time, their peaks may appear unexpectedly during the analysis of the second or third sample or even later. Fortunately, it is usually easy to recognize such peaks because they are much broader

than the neighboring peaks, frequently so broad
that they cause apparent upward then downward baseline drift.

A similar source for artifacts may be material
which has come out of solution somewhere in the
system, but outside the column. The most probable
such place is the connection between the column
end and the injector, or in the injector itself.
Part of this material may slowly back-diffuse into
the column and be eluted from there during gradient
programming, or after the mobile phase or its
composition was changed. The corresponding peaks
will not always be broader than the neighboring
peaks and, therefore, their recognition is more
difficult. If one suspects the presence of such
erroneous peaks, the easiest way to check them is
to carry out a second programmed "analysis" in
the same range and under the same conditions, but
without any sample. If artifact peaks are due to
this effect, then, most likely they will appear
during the second run.

If this artifact is experienced, the operator may
periodically flush the system with a solvent known
to dissolve the contaminants.

If solutions with the solvent present in excess
quantities are analyzed, the solvent peak will
quickly pass through the column at the beginning
of the analysis, and it represents a very high
concentration in the mobile phase passing through
the column. This large amount of solvent can
easily displace certain components of the liquid
phase or some adsorbed contaminations (e.g., from
previous samples) which, in turn, would emerge as
peaks in the chromatogram. A very special case
is the analysis of aqueous samples, particularly
if the components of interest are present in small
quantities in an excess of water. In such cases,
artifact peaks might well occur, particularly if
the separating mechanism in use is adsorption. In
order to avoid any misinterpretation of the chromatogram, it is always advisable to inject pure solvent or water into the instrument and analyze it
under identical conditions.

Finally, one more possibility for artifact·peaks should be mentioned: impurities in the allegedly pure solvent. These peaks are actually not "artifacts" because they are genuine constituents of the injected sample. In order to avoid any possible misinterpretation of the chromatogram obtained, one should always check the purity of the solvent used in sample preparation in a separate analysis.

Part Six:
Quantitative Analysis

After identifying the individual sample components, the next step is to determine the amount of some, or all of them. This is referred to as quantitative analysis.

Most quantitation in liquid chromatography is accomplished exactly as in gas chromatography: the strip chart recorder is an invaluable part of the system. The most simple units depend entirely on the strip chart trace, while more complex arrays of equipment may utilize sophisticated counting, integrating, and computing devices.

6.1 PEAK HEIGHT

All LC detectors produce an electrical signal which is utilized to either drive a meter movement or, most commonly, operate the pen of a recorder. The more light absorbed or deflected by the material passing through the detector cell, the stronger the signal. Thus, peak amplitude can be seen to be related to the response of the detector to the compounds passing through the cell, and peak height can be used an an indication of the amount of each component in the sample.

The advantages of using peak height for quantitative evaluation of the chromatogram are its simplicity and speed of calculation. Disadvantages are the tendency for peak heights to vary (much more than peak area) if chromatographic conditions vary, and loss of information if large peaks go off-scale. In addition, one must realize that in liquid chromatography, it is very unusual for any compounds to have equal response. This means that peak heights - just as area values - cannot be used in themselves for quantitation, but some additional means must be used to correct or standardize these values. These methods will be discussed below.

6.2 PEAK AREA MEASUREMENT

The use of peak area (A) for quantitative measurement is based on the fact that the amount of concentration (C) of a sample component is directly
proportional to it

$$C - fA \qquad\qquad (22)$$

The problem is that the peak has (ideally) a
Gaussian shape and thus, unless an electronic
integrator is used which automatically integrates
the area under the curve, the manual measurement
of the true peak area is tedious and difficult.
For this reason, approximation is often used.

6.21 MANUAL METHODS

Manual methods which were utilized to obtain the
true peak area included cutting out and weighing
the paper corresponding to the peak (and use its
weight in lieu of the area) or utilization of a
planimeter. The planimeter (see Figure 6-1C) has
a weighted anchor at one end; a magnifying glass
or pointer at the other, which is used to trace
along the outlines of the curve, and a pivoted
center section. The center section contains a
roller and numerical indicator which accumulates
area information as the pointer is moved around
the circumference of the peak. The proper use of
a planimeter requires considerable skill and experience and, even so, obtaining accurate results
requires repetitive tracings on each peak with
the totals averaged. Obviously, this is a very
time-consuming procedure.

Due to the problems of manually obtaining the true
peak area, several approximation methods are used
in practice (cf. Figure 6-1). The most frequently
used method multiplies the peak width at half
height (w_h) with the peak height measured at maximum (h_{max}). This is the most widely used and
most accurate method.* The other two possibilities
are to carry out a kind of triangulation, calculating the area of the isosceles formed by the
peak width at the base with either the two lines
connecting its ends with the peak maximum, or the
two tangents drawn to the inflection points of

---

* Naturally, assuming that distances are measured
properly; cf. Figure 2-3.

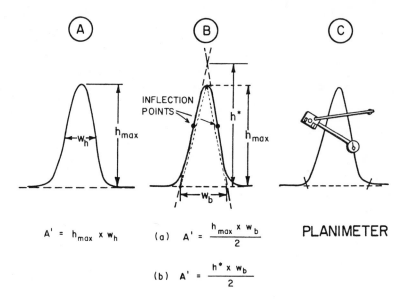

Fig. 6-1. Ways to obtain peak area values.

the Gaussian peak. The problem with both these methods is that the establishment of the tangents and hence, the peak width at base requires a graphical interpretation and is prone to error.

None of these calculation methods gives the true peak area of the peak, but only a value representing a fraction of it and Table 6-1 gives the corresponding values. This does not represent a problem as long as each peak is calculated in the same way and none of the peaks show asymmetry.

Obtaining precise results with any of these quantitating methods requires a high degree of operator skill. Table 6-2 summarizes the results of a comparative study of the primary quantitative methods. Operators who establish a high degree of skill in a particular method may be able to attain precision much higher than that shown here and, thus, may justify their favorite system. In almost any similar study, however, the utmost accuracy will generally be shown to be achieved with the use of electronic integration.

Table 6-1. Calculated Peak Area Values as Percentage of the True Area Value.*

CALCULATION METHOD **	AREA OBTAINED AS % OF THE TRUE AREA
$h_{max} \times w_h$	93.9%
$\dfrac{h_{max} \times w_b}{2}$	79.9%
$\dfrac{h^* \times w_b}{2}$	96.9%

* Assuming Gaussian peaks.

** w_h = peak width at half height; w_b = peak width at base; h_{max} = peak height at its maximum; $h^* = 1.214 \times h_{max}$. See also Figure 5-2.

Table 6-2. Comparison of Precision of Peak Area Measurement.

METHOD	TIME NEEDED FOR EVALUATION AND CALCULATION*	PRECISION %
Planimeter	15 min	4.06
Triangulation based on peak width at base	12 min	4.06
Peak height at max. x peak width at half height	10 min	2.58
Cut and weigh	20 min	1.74
Disk integrator	5 min	1.29
Digital integrator	instantaneous	0.44

* Typical 3-peak analysis.

6.22   PEAK AREA INTEGRATION

Integration means to continuously monitor the
strength of the signal (peak amplitude) as a function of time, in this way, determining the area
under the signal-vs.-time curve.

6.221   PLOTTING INTEGRATORS

The most simple and inexpensive integrators are
those which attach to the recorder and while not
giving a direct area count, present readouts from
which the area can directly be estimated. A typical representative of this group of readout
devices is the so-called Disc integrator. Today,
it is of historical interest only; yesterday, it
represented an important step in the evolution of
chromatographic data systems. The Disc integrators
use a special recorder paper with a separate scale
at one end and a separate pen drawing a straight
baseline when the actual recorder pen is on the
baseline and moving back-and-forth when the
recorder pen deviates from this baseline. The more
intense the signal (i.e., larger the peak), the
more rapid the integrator pen movement, hence, the
more zig-zag lines drawn by the integrator pen. By
counting these lines corresponding to a peak, a
number proportional to the actual peak area can be
established.

The basic shortcoming of a Disc integrator is
that it is too slow for very short peaks. All
peaks must be on-scale and if the baseline
drifts, it is very difficult to estimate the
counts contributed by the baseline drift. These
shortcomings are eliminated by the use of digital
integrators.

6.222   DIGITAL INTEGRATORS

Digital integrators are normally connected directly to the detector amplifier, in series between
it and the recorder. They monitor the output of
the detector and accumulate numerical information
as components passing through the detector produce a signal. The data is normally printed out
on a continuous roll of paper. Even the most

simple digital integrators can be adjusted to compensate for drifting baselines and also continue to accumulate data when large peaks go offscale on the recorder. The more complex units may be pre-programmed to compensate for almost any chromato-graphic anomaly such as unresolved peaks, tailing peaks, shoulders, etc. Simple units will at least total the components; the more complex may be programmed to automatically correct each component by a preselected correction factor, and the most sophisticated units can be programmed to provide comprehensive analytical reports, complete with component names, the date and time, and even the name of the operator.

6.223   DATA SYSTEMS WITH PRINTER/PLOTTERS

The most recently developed systems not only provide all the information previously obtainable only from the most sophisticated digital integra-tors, but also have full computer capability which allows the unit to provide complex multiple anal-yses, including the ability to operate other in-struments, switch devices at preselected times, and manipulate the data obtained. Also, these systems employ high-speed printing heads which continuously plot the chromatogram on thermally activated paper simultaneously recording certain important values such as retention time, attenu-ations, baseline correction methods, integration start and stop points, and, at the end of the analysis, provide a full report including all of the pertinent information such as retention time, peak area, corrected peak area (utilizing pre-determined response factors stored in the memory of the system), concentration of the individual sample components and their identification. The SIGMA 10 Chromatography Data Station of Perkin-Elmer is an outstanding example of this type of data system.

6.3   QUANTITATIVE INTERPRETATION OF A CHROMATOGRAM

After obtaining the area of the individual peaks, the next step is to establish the amount or con-centration of each sample component present corre-

esponding to these peaks. Depending on the analytical problem, the chromatographer may want to
establish this for every sample component producing a peak in the chromatogram or, only for one
or a few sample components.

6.31   INTERNAL NORMALIZATION

In this case, one is calculating the concentration
(amount) for every sample component, and one is
assuming that

- each sample component is producing a peak; and

- that the detector will give the same area for
  each sample component if present in the same
  concentration.

If a solvent peak is present, it is common to dis-
regard the area of this peak when totalling the
areas and consider the areas of the peaks corresponding to the actual sample components only.

If the detector response for equal amounts (concentrations) of the sample components is the same,
then the so-called relative peak areas (A%) are
assumed to be equal to the concentration of the
respective component in the sample.

Normalization is accomplished by dividing the
area of each peak by the total area (or total
minus solvent peak area) and multiplying by 100:

$$A_1 + A_2 + \ldots A_i + \ldots A_n = \sum_{i=1}^{n} A_i \quad (23)$$

$$C_i\% = A_i\% = \frac{A_i}{\sum_{i=1}^{n} A_i} \, 100 \quad (24)$$

6.32   COMPARISON WITH SAMPLES OF KNOWN CONCENTRATION

This is the simplest calibration technique and is
based on the linearity of detector response: e.g.,
twice the amount gives twice the peak area. It is
particularly advantageous if limited numbers of

samples are to be analyzed and thus, the determination of response factors or calibration plots
is too time-consuming.

The method has two versions. In the first case, a
number of, or all sample components may be determined while in the second case, only one or a
few components are analyzed.

6.321 BRACKETING TECHNIQUE

In this technique, first, an approximate composition of the sample is established. Next, a
synthetic sample of similar composition is prepared and analyzed under identical conditions. The
peak areas are compared with those obtained for
the original sample and the actual composition
calculated.

As mentioned, the method is based on the propor-
tionality of the amounts present with the corresponding peak areas. Thus, if subscript s refers
to the sample and st to the synthetic sample,
then

$$C_s/C_{st} = A_s/A_{st} \qquad (25a)$$

$$C_s = (A_s/A_{st})\, C_{st} \qquad (25b)$$

Since generally we are interested in concentrations rather than absolute amounts, we are also
introducing the actual sample amounts (w_s and w_{st})
and the concentrations of the individual compounds
($C_s\%$ and $C_{st}\%$):

$$C_s\% = (C_s/w_s)\, 100 \qquad (26a)$$

$$C_{st}\% = (C_{st}/w_{st})\, 100 \qquad (26b)$$

Substituting eq. (26a)-(26b) into eq.(25b), we
obtain the following expression to calculate the
concentration of the compound of interest in the
actual sample.

$$C_s\% = \frac{A_s}{A_{st}} \; \frac{w_{st}}{w_s} \; (C_{st}\%) \qquad (27)$$

Naturally, this calculation can be performed for each sample component.

6.322 COMPARISON WITH AN EQUAL-VOLUME STANDARD

This method is particularly useful if only the concentration (amount) of a single component is to be determined. However, it requires the reproducible injection of equal sample volumes. Therefore, it is advisable to first inject repetitive volumes of the standard solution to see whether the repeated analyses agree with the confidence limits required. A mechanical injection valve or auto-sampling device is recommended; however, a meticulous worker using a good syringe can inject repetitively with a relative standard deviation of less than 1.0%.

The technique is simple and fast and many samples can be analyzed with little preparation. However, the problem is that both the chromatographic system and the operator must be highly precise and reliable. Normally, samples should be analyzed in duplicate to ascertain system reliability.

The basis of the method is the same as of the bracketing technique. Since the sample volumes are identical, the peak areas obtained when analyzing the sample and the standard solution are directly proportional to the amount (concentration) of the component of interest. Using the same symbols as before, i.e., subscript s for the sample solution and st for the standard solution, A for the peak area and C for the amount present:

$$\frac{C_s}{C_{st}} = \frac{A_s}{A_{st}} \tag{28a}$$

and

$$C_s = \frac{A_s}{A_{st}} C_{st} \tag{28b}$$

Below, is an example of the determination of naphthalene in a sample.

(a) Establish the following analytical conditions:

Column: ODS (C_{18}) bonded phase

Mobile phase: 70:30 methanol-distilled water

Column temperature: 25°C

UV detector at 254 nm, 0.16 AUFS

(b) Prepare a standard solution by weighing 0.02 g of naphthalene into a 100-mL volumetric flask and diluting to 100 mL with chloroform. The concentration of this solution is

$$\frac{2 \times 10^{-2} \text{ g}}{100 \text{ mL}} = \frac{2 \times 10^4 \text{ µg}}{1 \times 10^5 \text{ µL}} = 0.2 \text{ µg/µL}$$

Thus a 5-µL aliquot of the solution represents 1.0 µg.

(c) Prepare sample solutions in 100 mL volumetric flasks in chloroform.

(d) Inject 5-µL aliquots of the two solutions and obtain the peak area. Here are the actual values obtained:

naphthalene peak (sample) 3830 counts
naphthalene peak (standard) 2000 counts

(e) Calculate amount of naphthalene present:

$$\frac{3830}{2000} \times 1.0 = 1.91 \text{ mg}$$

If a number of sample unknowns containing widely varying concentrations of the component of interest are to be analyzed, the system must be examined for linearity. This is done by preparing standard solutions of differing concentrations, preferably with the lowest less than the smallest unknown, and the larger, greater than the highest unknown. Thus, in the previous example, it would be wise to prepare a 0.3 or 0.4 µg/µL standard to ascertain that the area/concentration is linear above the 0.2 µg/µL standard.

If the linearity of the amount vs. peak area relationship is demonstrated, one may even prepare plots showing this. Subsequently, unknown samples can be analyzed without an additional analysis of a standard solution and the amounts corresponding to the compounds of interest read from these plots. Naturally, an absolute reproducibility of analytical conditions and sample volumes is positively necessary for this.

6.33   UTILIZATION OF DETECTOR RESPONSE FACTORS

In liquid chromatography, it is relatively uncommon for all components of a mixture to have equal detector response. This is especially true with UV detectors where correction factors may vary by thousands. Fortunately, in practical cases, the variation is usually much less especially when a wavelength is used at which many components have some adsorption, such as the strong 200 nm area where some variable wavelength detectors can be operated.

The detector response factors (f) establish the relationship between peak area (A) and concentration (C):

$$C_i = f_i A_i \qquad (29)$$

The easiest way to determine these factors is to analyze a standard mixture having each component present in equal concentrations. For example, let us assume a three-component mixture: analyzing this sample, we obtain the respective peak area values of A_1, A_2, A_3.

We can now write eq. (29) for each component:

$$C_1 = f_1 A_1 \qquad (30a)$$

$$C_2 = f_2 A_2 \qquad (30b)$$

$$C_3 = f_3 A_3 \qquad (30c)$$

Since the concentrations are equal, we can write:

$$C_1 = C_2 = C_3 \qquad (31)$$

$$f_1 A_1 = f_3 A_3 \qquad (32a)$$

$$f_2 A_2 = f_3 A_3 \qquad (32b)$$

and

$$\frac{f_1}{f_3} = \frac{A_3}{A_1} \qquad (33a)$$

$$\frac{f_2}{f_3} = \frac{A_3}{A_2} \qquad (33b)$$

We now establish the third component as the "norm", assigning a response value of $f_3 = 1.00$ to it. Hence, the <u>relative</u> <u>response</u> <u>factors</u> can be calculated as the ratio of two peak areas:

$$f_1 = \frac{A_3}{A_1} \qquad (34a)$$

$$f_2 = \frac{A_2}{A_2} \qquad (34b)$$

Now, when analyzing a sample consisting of these three components which are present in unknown concentrations, the following respective peak areas are obtained: A_1^*, A_2^*, A_3^*. The corresponding concentrations ($C\%$) are calculated in the following way, utilizing the predetermined response factors:

$$A_1^* f_1 + A_2^* f_2 + \ldots A_i^* f_i + \ldots A_n^* f_n = \sum_{i=1}^{n} A_n^* f_i \qquad (35)$$

$$C_i\% = \frac{A_i^* f_i}{\sum\limits_{i=1}^{n} A_i^* f_i} \; 100, \; \text{etc.} \qquad\qquad (36)$$

Below, is an example of the step-by-step procedure of the analysis of a tablet containing aspirin, caffeine, and phenacetin including the determination of the response factors:

(a) Establish the following analytical conditions:

   Column: 25 cm x 2.6 mm ID ODS (C_{18}) bonded phase

   Mobile phase: 30:70 acetonitrile-distilled water; 1 mL/min

   Column temperature: 70°C

   UV detector at 254 nm, 0.2 AUFS (about x8 on detectors with binary attenuators)

(b) Prepare a standard solution by weighing 200 mg each of aspirin, caffeine, and phenacetin into a 100-mL volumetric flask and dilute to volume with reagent-grade methanol. The solution will contain 0.2 μg/μL of each component:

$$\frac{0.2g}{1\times10^3 \; mL} = \frac{0.2\times10^6 \; \mu g}{1\times10^6 \; \mu L} = 0.2 \; \mu g/\mu L$$

(c) Make several successive 5-μL injections of the standard solution and obtain the areas of the peaks. Figure 6-2 shows a typical chromatogram. Average the peak area values. Here are the actual values obtained:

aspirin	238	counts
caffein	660	"
phenacetin	1190	"

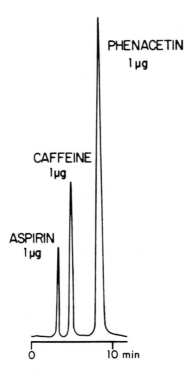

Fig. 6-2. *Chromatograms of the standard solution used to establish the detector response factors for internal normalization.*

(d)　Establish the relative response factors (f) by using one of the three as the norm (f=1.00):

aspirin　f $= \dfrac{1190}{238} = 5.0$

caffein　f $= \dfrac{1190}{660} = 1.8$

(e)　Prepare an actual sample in the following way: crush one table in a mortar with a pestle and transfer to a 100-mL volumetric flask; dilute to volume with methanol. Shake the flask to dissolve; be sure to allow undissolved solids to settle prior to withdrawal of a sample aliquot into the syringe or blockage may occur.

(f) Inject 5-µL of the sample solution under
the same operating conditions used for
response factor determination. If in doubt
about peak identification, make up some
samples of pure standards and compare
retention times calculated from the chromatogram of the sample and the chromatogram
of the standards.

Determine the peak areas; multiply each
with the respective response factor,
total the corrected areas and calculate
the percentage of each corrected area in
the total. This will be equal to composition (wt%) in the original sample:

```
aspirin:      90 counts   90x5.0 = 450.0
caffein:     265    "     265x1.8 = 477.0
phenacetin: 460    "     460x1.0 = 460.0
                                   _____
                                    1387.0
```

aspirin: $C = \dfrac{450}{1387} \; 100 = 32.4\%$

caffein: $C = \dfrac{477}{1387} \; 100 = 34.4\%$

phenacetin: $C = \dfrac{460}{1387} \; 100 = \underline{33.2\%}$

100.0%

Once correction factors have been established, it
is a simple matter to analyze different analgesic
compounds for differences in composition. It is
also possible to analyze beverages for caffeine
content using the same conditions.

6.34 INTERNAL STANDARD METHODS

Internal standard methods are generally used when
the analyst is interested only in the concentration
of one or a few sample components. There are three
internal standard methods in common use:

- the classical method, where a weighed portion
  of the standard is combined with the weighed
  sample;

- the stock solution method, used when the same

materials are analyzed frequently, and a stock solution of standard is made up and pipetted into the sample or is used as the diluent for the sample;

• the calibration plot method, where a series of standards are run and a concentration curve is plotted based on corrected area.

6.341 WEIGHED INTERNAL STANDARD METHOD

This method is based essentially on the same considerations as the previous calculations. If we have two components present in the sample in different amounts, then eq. (29) can be written for both components:

$$C_2 = f_2 A_2 \qquad (37)$$

$$C_1 = f_1 A_1 \qquad (38)$$

If component 2 is the internal standard to which we assign a response factor of $f_2 = 1.00$ then, dividing the two equations, we get (using subscript st for the standard and i for the component of interest):

$$\frac{C_{st}}{C_i} f_i = \frac{A_{st}}{A_i} \qquad (39)$$

If we want to determine the relative response factor of component i, we analyze a sample in which both amounts C and C_i are known. Thus, obtaining the respective peak area values of A_{st} and A_i, the relative response factor f_i can be calculated:

$$f_i = \frac{C_i}{C_{st}} \cdot \frac{A_{st}}{A_i} \qquad (40)$$

Conversely, if f_i had already been determined, analyzing a sample with an unknown amount of component i, to which a known amount of the internal standard was added, we can directly calculate C_i:

$$C_i = \frac{A_i}{A_{st}} C_{st} f_i \qquad (41)$$

In utilizing the internal standard method, it is convenient to have approximately the same amount of both components present so that the same detector settings may be used during analysis. This avoids erroneous results which may be due to non-linear detectors.

The following example for the determination of cocaine in a sample utilizing codeine as the internal standard, illustrates the weighed internal standard method:

(a) Establish the following analytical conditions:

Column: 25 cm x 2.6 mm ID Sil-X-I fluoroether bonded phase

Mobile phase: 90:10 acetonitrile-water containing 0.3% H_3PO_4; 2 mL/min

Column temperature: room temperature

UV detector at 210 nm, 0.1 AUFS

(b) Prepare a standard solution by weighing 12.0 mg of codeine (internal standard) and 11.3 mg of cocaine into a 100-mL volumetric flask and dilute to volume with distilled water.

(c) Make successive 2-µL injections of this standard solution and obtain the area of the peaks. Average the peak area values. Here are the actual values obtained:

codeine: 1009 counts
cocaine: 635   "

(d) Establish the relative response factor (f) for cocaine:

$$f = \frac{11.3}{12.0} \quad \frac{1009}{635} = 1.50$$

(e)   Prepare an actual sample in the following way: Into a 100-mL volumetric flask, weigh known amounts of the sample and the internal standard and dilute to volume as above. The actual amounts were:

> sample: 59.8 mg
> codeine: 11.0 mg

(f)   Inject 2-µL of this sample solution under the same operating conditions as used for the response factor determination. Determine the peak area and carry out the calculation as given below:

> peak area values: codeine: 990 counts
>   cocaine: 1031   "

Amount of cocaine present:

$$\frac{1031}{990} \, (11.0) \, (1.50) = 17.18 \text{ mg}$$

Concentration of cocaine in sample:

$$\frac{17.18}{59.8} \, 100 = 28.73\%$$

6.342   STOCK SOLUTION METHOD

In this method, a stock solution consisting of the internal standard and the component of interest is analyzed separately under identical conditions as the sample solution to which the internal standard is added in the same concentration as in the stock solution. Writing eq. (26) for each component in either solution, it can be deduced that the concentration of the component of interest in the sample solution can be calculated as follows: (subscript i refers to this component and st to the internal standard; (anal.) refers to the sample solution and (stock) to the stock solution):

$$C_i\% = \frac{A_{st}(\text{stock})}{A_i(\text{stock})} \; \frac{A_i(\text{anal.})}{A_{st}(\text{anal.})} \; C_i\% \,(\text{stock}) \qquad (42)$$

By knowing the weight of the sample and the dilution of the sample solution, the concentration of the component of interest in the sample can be calculated.

6.343 INTERNAL STANDARD PLOT METHOD

In this method, a series of standard mixtures containing the same amount of the internal standard but varying amounts of the compound of interest, are analyzed and the peak area determined. It is obvious that the ratios of the areas (A_i/A_s) will be related to the ratios of the respective weights; as long as one is working in the linear range of the detector and did not overload the column, the corresponding plot will be linear.

This plot is then used to determine the (unknown) amount of the compound of interest present in actual samples. An equal amount of the internal standard is added to each sample, the mixtures are analyzed under identical conditions, and the respective area ratios calculated. With the help of these, one can directly read the corresponding weight ratios from the calibration plot. Knowing the amount of internal standard added, the amount of the compound of interest can be calculated.

Below is an example of this method. The samples consist of mixtures of dimethyl phthalate (DMP) and diethyl diphenyl urea (EPU) to which acetanilide (ACA) is given as the internal standard. The step-by-step procedure is given below.

  (a)   Establish the following analytical
        conditions:

        Column: 25 cm x 2.6 mm ID Silica A

        Mobile phase: dichloromethane containing
                         0.1-0.5% isopropanol;
                         2 mL/min

        Column temperature: room temperature

        UV detector at 254 nm, 0.2 AUFS

(b)   Establishment of the calibration plot:

Make up three standard sample solutions by weighing the amounts listed in Table 6-3 into 100-mL volumetric flasks and diluting them to volume with the mobile phase. Inject 1.0 µL of each standard solution and determine the peak area. The values obtained are listed in Table 6-4.

Calculate the needed weight and area ratios; these are listed in Table 6-5.

Plot the area ratios vs. the weight ratios for each component. Figures 6-3 and 6-4 show the corresponding plots.

Table 6-3.   Amounts of Substances Weighed Into a 100-mL Volumetric Flask for the Establishment of the Calibration Plot.

SUBSTANCE	SAMPLE 1	SAMPLE 2	SAMPLE 3
Dimethyl phthalate	0.050 g	0.125 g	0.200 g
Diethyl diphenylurea	0.030 g	0.065 g	0.100 g
Acetanilide*	0.100 g	0.100 g	0.100 g

* Internal Standard

Table 6-4.   Peak Area Obtained When Analyzing a 1 µL Aliquot of the Three Standard Solutions.

SUBSTANCE	SAMPLE 1 (COUNTS)	SAMPLE 2 (COUNTS)	SAMPLE 3 (COUNTS)
Dimethyl phthalate	151	387	622
Diethyl diphenylurea	470	1035	1553
Acetanilide	1685	1660	1668

*Internal Standard

Table 6-5. Weight and Area Ratios Needed for the
Establishment of the Calibration Plots.*

	SAMPLE 1	SAMPLE 2	SAMPLE 3
Area DMP / Area ACA	$\frac{151}{1685} = 0.090$	$\frac{387}{1660} = 0.233$	$\frac{622}{1668} = 0.373$
Weight DMP / Weight ACA	$\frac{0.050}{0.100} = 0.50$	$\frac{0.125}{0.100} = 1.250$	$\frac{0.200}{0.100} = 2.000$
Area EPU / Area ACA	$\frac{470}{1685} = 0.279$	$\frac{1035}{1660} = 0.624$	$\frac{1553}{1668} = 0.931$
Weight EPU / Weight ACA	$\frac{0.030}{0.100} = 0.30$	$\frac{0.065}{0.100} = 0.650$	$\frac{0.100}{0.100} = 1.00$

* DMP = dimethyl phthalate; EPU = diethyl diphenyl urea;
  ACA = acetanilide (internal standard).

(c)   Sample analysis:

To a given weight of sample to be analyzed,
add 0.100 g of acetanilide (internal
standard) and dilute to volume in a 100-mL
volumetric flask. It is most convenient to
prepare such a stock solution of acetanilide
and use this solution to make up the sample
to 100 mL.

Inject 1.0-µL of the sample solution and
obtain areas for both the substances of
interest and the standard. Calculate the
proper area ratios and read from the proper
plot the weight ratio corresponding to the
respective area ratio. Multiplying this
with 0.1 (the weight of acetanilide), the
actual weight of the component of interest
is obtained. Knowing the sample amount ,
the concentration is calculated.

The following values represent an actual
analysis:

sample weight: 0.500 g

added acetanilide: 0.100 g
peak area values:
DMP	511	counts
EPU	881	"
ACA	1671	"

The calculated peak area ratios:

DMP/ACA	0.306
EPU/ACA	0.527

In Figure 6-3, an area ratio of 0.306 corresponds to a weight ratio of 1.62:

$$\frac{\text{weight DMP}}{\text{weight ACA}} = 1.62$$

Since the weight of acetanilide added was 0.100 g, the weight of dimethyl phthalate is 1.62 x 0.1 = 0.162 g. The sample weight was 0.500 g; thus, the concentration (wt%) of DMP in the sample is

$$\frac{(0.162)\ (100)}{0.5} = 32.4\%$$

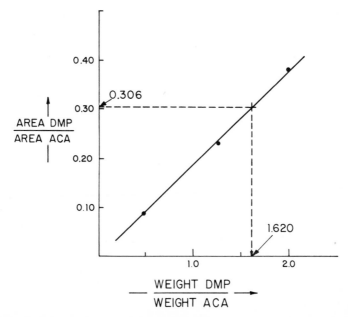

Fig. 6-3. Calibration plot for dimethyl phthalate (DMP); internal standard: acetanilide (ACA).

In Figure 6-4, an area ratio of 0.527 corresponds to a weight ratio of 0.56:

$$\frac{\text{weight EPU}}{\text{weight ACA}} = 0.56$$

Thus, the weight of dimethyl diphenyl urea is 0.56 x 0.1 = 0.056 g, representing a concentration (wt%) of

$$\frac{(0.056)\ (100)}{0.5} = 11.2\%$$

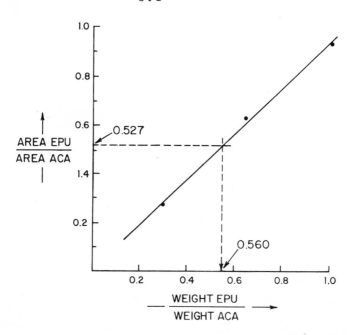

Fig. 6-4. *Calibration plot for diethyl diphenylurea (EPU); internal standard: acetanilide (ACA).*

6.35 EXTERNAL STANDARD METHODS

The term "external standard method" is not precise and is open to interpretation. In general, a number of calculation methods may be characterized by it.

The first is a simple extension of the weighed internal standard method. This may be used e.g., if the chromatogram of the sample is so "crowded" that there is no place for the peak of an internal standard. In such a case, it is convenient to prepare a separate solution of the internal standard and inject consecutively an equal volume aliquot of the sample solution and the standard solution. If the volumes are identical, the peak area and the corresponding amount of the substance of interest in the standard solution can be directly used in eqs. (40) and (41).

The term "external standard method" is sometimes used for two methods discussed earlier: the stock solution method or the method based on the comparison of the sample with an equal-volume standard. After all, in either case, there is an "external standard" solution with known concentration, analyzed separately.

6.4 STATISTICAL EVALUATION OF RESULTS

Any quantitative analytical chemistry method involves taking a sample, analyzing it, and making inferences about the sample based on the results obtained from the analysis. In order to improve the reliability of his work, the analyst is generally always carrying out the analysis more than once and considers the mean of these determinations as the final result.

There are two important criteria of any analysis. First, it should be accurate, and secondly, it should have a good precision. Accuracy is defined as the correctness of the measurement, while precision is a measure of the reproducibility of the measurements. Accuracy of the measurement depends on the method and the calibration (i.e., determination of the correct detector response factors) while precision primarily reflects the quality of the instrumentation and data handling.

It is generally accepted in statistics to express the degree of precision by the standard deviation. The standard deviation (s) is calculated in the following way:

$$s = \sqrt{\frac{\sum\limits_{i=1}^{n} (X_i - \overline{X})^2}{n-1}} \tag{43}$$

where n is the number of measurements, X_i represents the individual values and $\bar{X}$ is the mean of the individual values:

$$X_1+X_2+\ldots X_i+\ldots X_n = \sum_{i=1}^{n} X_i \qquad (44)$$

$$\bar{X}= \frac{\sum\limits_{i=1}^{n} X_i}{n} \qquad (45)$$

The <u>relative standard deviation</u> (s%), or using the older expression of coefficient of variation, expresses the standard deviation as percent of the mean value:

$$s\% = \frac{s}{\bar{X}}100 \qquad (46)$$

It should be mentioned that many times the symbol σ is used for the standard deviation and σ% for the relative standard deviation. This is, however, not correct since, in statistics sigma (σ) represents the standard deviation of a population or a distribution curve which is calculated using n instead of (n-1) in the denominator of Eq. (43).

Table 6-6 illustrates the statistical evaluation of five consecutive determinations. Today, such calculations can be carried out very quickly with the help of the sophisticated pocket calculators.

For a chromatographer who is carrying out a large number of quantitative determinations, it is very useful to have some basic textbook discussing the principles of statistics available. There are a number of such books; we recommend the following:

E.L. Bauer, A Statistical Manual for Chemists. Academic Press, New York and London; 2nd ed. 1971.

Table 6-6.   Example for the Statistical
Evaluation of Analytical Results.

NO.	ANALYTICAL RESULT X	$X - \overline{X}$	$(X - \overline{X})^2$
1	40.11	0.17	0.0289
2	40.50	0.22	0.0484
3	40.20	0.08	0.0064
4	40.15	0.13	0.0169
5	40.44	0.16	0.0256
TOTALS	201.40	0.76	0.1262

$\overline{X} = 201.40 \ / \ 5 = 40.28$

$s = \sqrt{\dfrac{0.1262}{5-1}} = 0.178$

$s\% = (0.178 \ / \ 40.28) \ 100 = 0.44\%$

Appendix I.
Guide to Column Connections for Liquid Chromatography

INTRODUCTION

In the rapidly expanding field of liquid chromatography, it is occasionally expedient to use columns
and instruments of different manufacture, since,
to-date, due to variations in source materials and
manufacturing procedures, no one company may be able
to provide the best column for every separation.
Unfortunately for the chromatographer, while most
columns are joined with identical 1/16-in. OD tubing,
there are several different types of column connectors
and end fittings in use to which the tubing must be
attached.

The ability to adapt columns to instruments (and
instruments to columns) is a key consideration in
obtaining full-range chromatography, yet improperly
connected columns can significantly reduce the overall
efficiency of the system.

COLUMN END FITTINGS

All column end fittings in current use are designed
for 1/16 in. OD connecting tubes with different internal
diameters. Three main types of such end fittings are
common; these are described briefly below, while their
schematics* are shown in Figs. 7-1 through 7-3. Note the
low-volume passage [which may vary from as much as
0.018-in. (0.4572 mm) to as little as 0.010-in.
(0.254 mm)] which connects the 1/16 -in. OD tube to
the fritted packing retainer. Some fittings are
"drilled out" so that the 1/16 in. OD tube rests
direcly on the frit.

---

* On these and subsequent figures in this Appendix,
the Perkin-Elmer part numbers of the individual pieces
are also given for convenience.

Externally Threaded Swagelok ®. These column end
fittings utilizing 1/4 in. nuts are reputed to be the
most widely used in present-day liquid chromatographs.
There are no special technical reasons for this and
their widespread use is purely historical: as modern
liquid chromatography evolved from gas chromatography,
many existing GC parts were simply modified to meet
the demands of LC. There is little advantage to this
type of connector except their very prevalence: they
are relatively fragile and difficult to seal and reseal
frequently without damage to threads.

Figure 7-1 shows the schematic of such an end fitting.
These are used on Perkin-Elmer Shodex GPC columns and
on many columns available from independent suppliers.

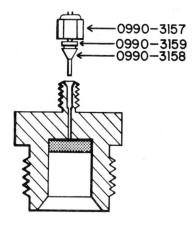

*Fig. 7-1. Externally threaded Swagelok ® column
end fitting.*

Perkin-Elmer's Externally Threaded Parker-Hannifin.
These column end fittings utilizing 7/16 in. nuts are
considered as an improvement over the previous one,
since a heavier seat and thread is used, allowing
innumberable connect-disconnect cycles without
damage or leaking.

Figure 7-2 shows the schematic of such an end fitting.
This type is used on Perkin-Elmer analytical and Vit-X
GPC columns.

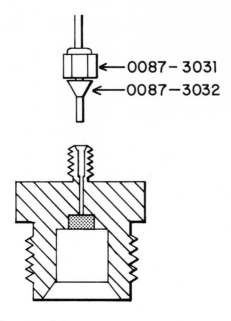

Fig. 7-2. *Perkin-Elmer's externally threaded Parker-Hannifin column end fitting.*

Internally Threaded Column End Fittings. Several manufacturers produce these end fittings which utilize 1/4-in. nuts. They will probably become the most widely used fittings in the future, since efficiency-stealing internal volume can be best controlled with this design.

Figure 7-3 shows the schematic of such a column end fitting. These are produced by various suppliers. Most use 10-32 thread size on nut, but utilize differ-ent ferrules; however, with the exception of Waters' Associates, the tube-stop depth (distance from bottom edge of taper to bottom of 1/16-in. clearance) is fairly identical. Improperly assembled or mismatched end fittings may either fail to seal, or may intro-duce a large void volume in the system if tubing does not seat in the bottom of the fitting.

It is critical that, unless it is determined that ferrule seats and tube depth are precisely identical, lines with swaged-in-place nuts and ferrules must only be used on fittings of the same design as that to which they were originally fitted. When in doubt, a new connector should be made.

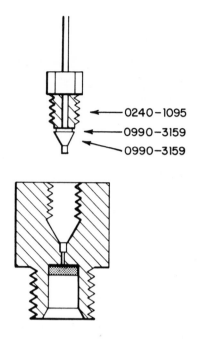

0240-1095

0990-3159

0990-3159

Fig. 7-3.   Internally threaded column end fitting.

ADAPTER CONSTRUCTION

There are two primary methods of providing instrument/
column adaptation. Both methods will result in each
column having its own individual inlet and outlet lines
and the difference is in the construction of the
connection of these lines.

The first method is recommended when <u>column change is
relatively infrequent</u>. In this case, construct a
separate injector-to-column, and column-to-detector
line for each type of column which utilizes different
end fittings. It is generally agreed that one should
<u>never</u> remove end fittings from columns unless there
is a problem with them, because the column may never
exhibit its original efficiency after the packing near
an end fitting is disturbed. This is especially true
of the lower end fitting which supports the packing
bed.

These adapters are constructed by selecting a length
of narrow bore (0.010 or 0.015 in. I.D., 0.254 or
0.381 mm) tubing similar to that used in the original

setup, and fitting nuts and ferrules on each end to
match the end fittings already on the instrument and
column. If columns are changed frequently, there may
be some danger of stripping or cross-threading
injector or detector fittings, however, and the use
of the following adapation is recommended.

The second method is recommended when column change
is frequent. In this case, modify the inlet (injector
to column) and outlet (column to detector) lines by
installing the so-called Zero-Dead-Colume (ZDV)
connectors. Once a ZDV union is in the line, separate
union-to-column lines can be constructed for each
different type of column. Any threaded parts which
become worn from intensive use can be easily and
inexpensively replaced.

Figure 7-4 shows the basic cross-sectional schematic
of a ZDV union. Note the small (0.010-0.015 in.)
connector passage between bottoms of 1/16-in. holes.
Some ZDV unions are drilled out so that 1/16-in. OD

Fig. 7-4. Cross sectional schematic of a Zero-Dead-
Volume (ZDV) union (Perkin-Elmer 0990-3807).

connector tubes can butt against one another. However,
if this is done, tube ends must be cut with extreme
precision and unions should be retained on the tubes
to which they were fitted, since insertion depth can
vary from side-to-side.

ZDV unions may differ in their size and the size of
the nuts used with them. Three types used by
Perkin-Elmer are shown here. The Swagelok ZDV union
(Figure 7-5) utilizes 1/4-in. body and nuts. These
nuts and ferrules may interchange with many internally-
threaded end fittings. The other two types are the so-
called SSI (Scientific Systems, Inc.) ZDV unions
which have a 3/8-in. body and 5/16-in. nuts. They
differ in the diameter of the connector passage: it
is 0.010-in. for 0990-3259 and 0.015-in. for 0990-3275.

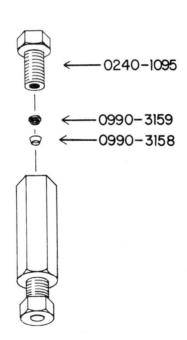

*Fig. 7-5. Connecting pieces used in the Swagelock
ZDV union (Perkin-Elmer 0990-3807).*

Nuts and ferrules interchange with most Perkin-Elmer LC detectors, pumps and accessory 1/16-in. bulkhead fittings and connectors. Peak broadening or tailing does not occur if larger bore tubing (i.e., 0.015-in. I.D.) is joined with a smaller bore union, but the converse may introduce noticeable effects if high-efficiency columns (10,000+ theoretical plates) are in use.

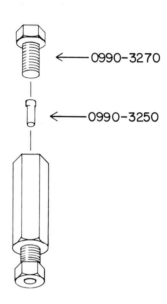

0990-3270

0990-3250

Fig. 7-6. *Connecting pieces used in the SSI (Scientific Systems, Inc.) ZDV union (Perkin-Elmer 0990-3259 and 0990-3274).*

As mentioned, two ZDV unions are needed to connect a column to the injector and detector, respectively. Figure 7-7 visualizes the complete system; the connectors at the column ends correspond to one of the three types discussed earlier.

Regardless of which type of adapters are used, operators should avoid the tendency to leave these in place without capping or sealing the ends of the column. It has generally been found that column life is shortened, sometimes significantly, if columns are allowed to dry out and when ends are not sealed, this may easily happen.

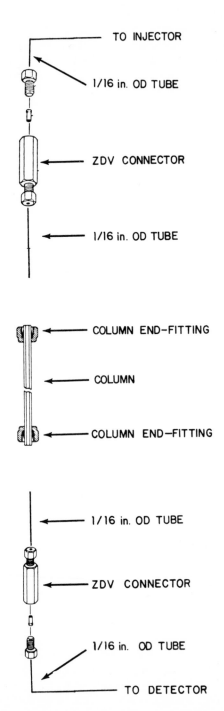

Fig. 7-7. Connection of a LC column to the liquid chromatograph.

PRECAUTIONS AND CONSIDERATIONS

The number one rule of any LC connection, from injector through detector, is that there be no unflushed volume, and that tubing and connector inner diameters be kept to a minimum and be as uniform as possible. While one can sometimes install lines fitted with ferrules of different manufacture from that of the union or column end fitting, it is critical that the tube end fits all the way to the bottom of the hole in the fitting and that the joint is leak-tight. Successful interchanging of ferrules and fittings is extremely difficult to achieve, and is generally not recommended.

The second advice given here is that the use of "adjustable" wrenches is avoided. These frequently do not maintain a tight fit, thus may slip off of, or "round off" the nuts. Also, use of adjustable wrenches encourages the misuse of long-handled wrenches on small connectors. The resultant high torque which is readily generated can easily strip even the strongest fittings. If, for any reason, adjustables are to be used, be sure to obtain high quality wrenches with jaws which do not work loose, and try to follow the following size recommendations to avoid damaging fittings:

nut	wrench
up to 3/8 in.	4-in.
7/16 - 5/8 in.	6-in.
5/8 - 1 in.	8-in.

Finally, the third advice concerns the cutting of the proper lengths of 1/16-in. tubing. Since butt-to-butt connections are required, it is very important that the tube is cut properly.

Below instructions for the proper tube cutting and ferrule installation are given.

TUBE CUTTING AND FERRULE INSTALLATION

Procedure for Cutting 1/16-in. OD Narrow-Bore Tubing.

(a) Support the tube in a vise or hold firmly in hand, or with pliers. (Avoid excessive pressure).

(b) With a triangular file, notch the tubing to about 1/3 of its depth. If skill in the use of the file is developed, the tube can be notched on several sides.

(c) Supporting the free end firmly, bend the tube back and forth several times until it breaks. (Be sure it bends only at the point where the cut has been made).

(d) Holding the tubing sideways to prevent filings from entering the opening, file the cut off end until it is flat and at a 90° angle. File gently in a manner which does not flare the tubing material across the opening. If this occurs, obtain a fine-point reaming tool (the point of a very sharp pin or thumbtack will do in an emergency) and open the hole to its original diameter.

(e) Blow out, or wash out, tubing before final installation to be sure all filings, etc., are removed from the line.

(f) Be sure no excessive metal extends beyond the 1/16-in. wall, or ferrules may not slip on.

NOTE: There are several commercial devices and accessories which aid in simplifying tube cutting. These are available from chromatographic accessory suppliers.

Procedure for Installation of Compression-Fitting Ferrules.

(a) Place the end fitting or union into which the tube is to be fitted in a vise, or hold firmly with a wrench. (It is best to hold the fitting with the hole facing up to help assure that the tube remains "bottomed" during installation).

(b) Slip nut and ferrule(s) over end of tube. Note that the larger diameter ends of all brands of ferrules are positioned so that they face the nut. Study the figures shown previously to assure proper arrangement of two-piece ferrules.

(c) Insert tube end into fitting. Be sure the tube extends to the seat bottom. Turn the nut down until it is finger-tight, then with a wrench, tighten an additional 1/4 to 1/3 more. (On Perkin-Elmer SSI nuts, this is to a torque of 40 to 50 inch-lb.).

(d) Install the assembled part and bring system up to operating pressure. Check for leaks. If a leak is noted, shut off pumps and tighten the nut an additional 5 foot-lb. (turn wrench through an arc of only 10 to 12 degrees).

(e) If leaks persist, disconnect the fitting and inspect the ferrule to determine if it is deformed or scarred. If so, cut off the end of the tube to which it is seated and install a new ferrule. Nuts can be reused as long as their threads are not stripped.

Appendix II.
Acknowledgements, Sources

Most of the figures and tables of this monograph were prepared specially for this purpose; however, a few were taken from previously published material. Below, the sources of these figures and tables are given. Reference numbers refer to the listing at the end of the Supplement.

The authors of this monograph gratefully acknowledge the cooperation of these sources permitting the reuse of the published material.

Figures

Fig. 2-1: 1; Fig. 2-2: 1; Fig. 2-4: 1;

Fig. 3-5: 2; Fig. 3-6: 2; Fig. 3-17: 3; Fig. 3-18: 2;

Fig. 3-22: 4; Fig. 3-24: 4; Fig. 3-28: 5; Fig. 3-31:

5; Fig. 3-33: 4; Fig. 3-35: 6.

Fig. 4-17: 7, 8; Fig. 4-19: 8, 9; Fig. 4-20: 10;

Fig. 4-21: 10; Fig. 4-22: 8, 11; Fig. 4-23: 8, 12;

Fig. 4-27: 13, Fig. 4-28: 14.

Tables

Table 3-3: 15; Table 3-10: 15; Table 4-2: 11;

Table 4-3: 16; Table 4-4: 17.

References

1. L.S. Ettre, Basic Relationships of Gas Chromatography. The Perkin-Elmer Corp., Norwalk, Conn., 1977.

2. R.W. Yost and R.D. Conlon, Selection of Optimum Solvent Systems in Adsorptive Liquid Chromatography. Chromatogr.Newslett. 1, 5-9 (1972).

3. L.R. Snyder, Principles of Adsorption Chromato-
    graphy. M. Dekker, Inc., New York, N.Y. 1968.

4. Anon., The Application of High-Speed, High-
    Efficiency Gel Permeation Chromatography.
    Technical Note - TN-89., The Perkin-Elmer Corp.,
    Norwalk, Conn.,1978.

5. Anon., Theory of Gel Permeation Chromatography.
    Technical Note - TN-86., The Perkin-Elmer Corp.,
    Norwalk, Conn., 1979.

6. W.E. Shumaker, LC Methods Development Procedure -
    A Description. Technical Note - TN-69., The
    Perkin-Elmer Corp., Norwalk, Conn., 1978.

7. R.W. Yost and W.M. MacLean, The Model LC-55 as
    an Universal Detector for Liquid Chromatography.
    Application Study - LCAS-56., The Perkin-Elmer
    Corp., Norwalk, Conn., 1975.

8. L.S. Ettre, Selective Detection in Column
    Chromatography. J.Chromatogr. Sci. 16, 396-417
    (1978).

9. R. Joester and H. Hein, A Preliminary Liquid
    Chromatography Study of the Analysis of Contra-
    ceptive Steroid Mixtures. Chromatogr.Newslett. 6,
    16 only (1978).

10. Anon., Model LC-75 Spectrophotometric Detector
    and LC-75 Autocontrol. Brochure No. L-579.
    The Perkin-Elmer Corp., Norwalk, Conn., 1979.

11. R.W. Yost, J. Stoveken and W. M. MacLean,
    Positive Peak Identification in Liquid Chromato-
    graphy Using Absorbance Ratioing With a Variable
    Wavelength Spectrophotometric Detector.
    J.Chromatogr. 134, 73-82 (1977).

12. A.T. Rhys-Williams and W. Slavin, Polycyclic
    Aromatic Hydrocarbons in Air Pollutants by HPLC
    and Fluorescence Detection. Chromatogr.Newslett.
    4, 28-31 (1976).

13. F.L. Vandemark, G.J. Schmidt and W. Slavin,
     Determination of Polyamines by Liquid Chromato-
     graphy and Precolumn Labelling for Fluorescence
     Detection. J.Chromatogr.Sci. 16, 465-469 (1978).

14. Anon., Model MPF-44B Fluorescence Spectrophoto-
     meter. Brochure No. L-561., The Perkin-Elmer
     Corp., Norwalk, Conn., 1978.

15. P.A. Bristow, LC in Practice, hetp, Inc.,
     Wilmslow, England, 1976.

16. W. West, Chemical Application of Spectroscopy.
     Interscience, New York, 1956; pg. 730.

17. R.F. Chen, Fluorescence of Dansyl Amino Acid in
     Organic Solvents and Protein Solutions. Arch.
     Biochem. Biophys. 120, 609-620 (1967).

WHAT IS
A WALL,
AFTER ALL?

For Lucy and Emily
J.A.

For Amelia
A.B.

First published 1993 by Walker Books Ltd
87 Vauxhall Walk, London SE11 5HJ

This edition published 2010

2 4 6 8 10 9 7 5 3 1

Text © 1993 Judy Allen
Illustrations © 1993 Alan Baron

The moral rights of the author and illustrator
have been asserted

This book has been typeset in Bembo Educational

Printed in China

British Library Cataloguing in Publication Data:
a catalogue record for this book is available from the British Library

ISBN 978-1-4063-1856-2

www.walker.co.uk